LINNÆUS IN GOTLAND

LINNÆUS IN GOTLAND

From the Diary at the Linnean Society, London,

to present-day Gotland

by Marita Jonsson   *photography* Marita and Helga Jonsson

translated from the Swedish by Eivor Cormack

GotlandsBoken

Öster=

Sjön

Öster=

Sjön

Feniken
Träsk
Afwe

Capell
Faleholm
Hau
Capellhamn
Baste
träsk
Fårön
Fleringe

Hall

Hangvar
Bunga
Stenkyrka
Rudhe
Lärbro
Fardums
Skeneholm
Lummelund
träsk
Furilen
Öfwerstequarn
Martebo
Othum
Tingsta
Olofsholm
Tingsta
Slyte=
Afundsholm
Träsk
hamn
Mego
Waskina
Lokrum
Strömar
Henum
Boga
Bro
Tielvard
WISBY
Fohlö
Heideby
Bähl

Wasterhede
Kiellinge
Endre
Walstena
Stenkumla
Foling bo
Bara
Tofta
Träkumla
Barlingbo
Gothem
Åkerbäk
Horsne
Eskelem
Dalem
Wall
Roma
Closter
Grundel
Hogren Biörke
Halla
Gantem
Attingebo
Norlanda
Masterby
Sionum
Wastergarns
Wastergarn
Wata
Wiklow
Anga
holme
Sanda
Wänge
Sågholm
Guldrop
Kräcklingebo
Ostergarns
Heide
Ahla
Torsburg
holme
Carlsöar
Klinta
Butla
Ostergarn
Gamelgarn
Froel
Ardra
Eitelem
Eysta
Loijsta
Ahlskog
Leveda
Gerum
Garda
Sproga
Fardum
Lyja
Träsk
Stånga
Silte
Hemsa
Burs
Näär
Alfwa
Hablingbo
Rona
Närholm
Habdum
Eke
Grönwik
Näs
Innerholm
Grötlingbo
Lytterholm
Fide
¼ ½ ¾ 1
2
Swenska Mijl.
Buswik
Sleswik
Stenbro
Öja
Hambre
Wamblingbo
Stockwik
Sundre
Hoburg
Heligholm

Charta
Öfwer
GOTLAND.

Contents

ITER

Gotlandicum

1741

Preface

The year 2007 is a year in the spirit of Linnæus, marking 300 years since his birth in the small home of the assistant rector at Råshult in the [Swedish] province of Småland and three centuries later, he is still Sweden's internationally best known natural historian. His system of classification for the identification of plants and animals was epoch-making and forms the basis of the modern scientific terminology. Linnæus, as he was called before being ennobled, is still a name commanding respect.

Ironically enough, the entire remains of his natural history property was bought and transported to England. At Burlington House in London, the Linnean Society administers his collections of books, herbaria, manuscripts and letters. The society safeguards his memory and ensures that his reputation lives on. Maybe it is because his estate ended up abroad that Linnæus became such a big name internationally.

In addition to his three houses that still exist and are open to the public – the home of his birth at Råshult with its 18th century landscape and gardens, his professorial residence with the show garden at Uppsala and his country house Hammarby with its garden – it is his writings and collections which are always highlighted, re-worked, commented on and published anew.

Linnæus's journeys through Sweden become topical once again because of the jubilee. He was the perfect natural historian for the powers that be in the Sweden of the Age of Enlightenment. With his

Portrait of Carl Linnæus painted by J.H. Scheffel, 1739

Left: The cover of the Diary, kept at the Linnean Society, Burlington House, London.

7

journeys to Lapland and Dalecarlia, he initiated the search for raw materials and unknown natural resources within the country and, in his capacity as president of the newly formed Royal Academy of Sciences, he made sure that the results were published and spread across Europe.

"Sweden is rich in everything", he stated in his introductory lecture as newly appointed professor at Uppsala. The year was 1741 and he had then just completed his third journey of exploration which had taken him to Öland and Gotland. There were to be two more such journeys, to the provinces of Västergötland and Scania. Common to them all was that Sweden's natural resources were to be investigated: minerals, types of soils, water quality, weather, plants, animals, manners and customs, everything that Enlightenment Sweden might be able to utilise. The wish-list was long and Linnæus showed the way. His journeys were spoken of widely. From having travelled alone on horseback through Lapland, he was already on his second journey accompanied by seven young men, wishing to help him explore Dalecarlia. There was a great deal to explore. He kept a diary, written and illustrated. His diary notes became the first draft of his reports which were later published, and his observations are also to be found in subject specific reports and books.

The purpose of his journey of exploration to Öland and Gotland was to search for plants and methods of dyeing, medicinal plants for the pharmacies and clays that could be used for clay-pipes and china.

Mr G A Rutensköld, public finance prosecutor and member of the Manufacture and Trade deputation, had already in January 1741 proposed that Linnæus should be allowed to make the journey in order to find "species of plants or grasses (…) which were either useful to the apothecaries or serviceable in the dye-works". Later, in February, when the matter was being dealt with in the parliament, Linnæus was summoned there, at which time he also expressed a wish to study minerals. The journey was granted approval; he was to receive a daily allowance for three months and horse conveyance.

For the journey Linnæus sought "young, bright and handsome youths" capable of assisting and helping him edit his diary.

Six young men accompanied him at their own expense. They were: Pehr Adlerheim economicus, born 1712; Fredrich Ziervogel geographicus, later apothecary, born 1727; Johan Moræus mineralogus, probationer at the mines authority *Bergskollegium*, born 1719; Hans Jakob Gahn domesticus and iron works proprietor, born 1719, and later treasurer at Falun, Gottfried Dubois zoologicus and later county medical officer in Stockholm, born 1725, and Samuel Wendt botanicus, born 1720.

Together with the youths – Ziervogel was only 14 years old – Carl Linnæus travelled around Gotland during one month in the summer of 1741. They left Stockholm on the 26th May (6th June according to our calendar) on horseback heading for Kalmar and Öland.

"Spring, which ought not be measured after Calendarium but after climate and warmth, was so far advanced that the maple had opened its flowers but not its leaves; that the birch had just opened and was flowering at its best. The stipules of the alder had recently burst open and the spruce had on its outermost branches little red buds like wild strawberries which were its male flowers, though not yet floury. Lime, oak and aspen were still deep in their winter slumber."

He arrived in Gotland on the 22nd June, a week later than planned, as the post yacht, which trafficked the stretch between Gaxa on Öland and Klintehamn, was in far too poor condition. Linnæus took no risks at sea. Through District Police Superintendent Sahlsten at the farm of Horn, he managed to hire a larger yacht to carry the party straight to Visby. According to our Gregorian calendar, introduced in Sweden in 1753, 11 days need to be added to the 1741 dates so that they agree with today's calendar. Thus Linnæus arrived in the island on the 3rd July.

The journey around Gotland was no tranquil pleasure trip. Linnæus was, during his summer journeys, always under pressure because of the brief period of flowering, the transformation from flower to fruit, the plant's withering. He wanted to see the plants in full bloom; now he was a week late – of great consequence in a brief Swedish summer. For the party, the Gotland journey meant long days beginning at dawn and sometimes lasting till 10 or 11 o'clock at night. They rarely allowed themselves a rest except on Sundays which were spent attending church services and in conversation with the rector or quietly wandering around the nearby rectory meadow. It is a tired, and at times stressed, Linnæus who emerges between the lines, and his own handwriting, or those of his students, is not always easy to decipher.

Linnæus travelled around the entire island, even out to islands such as Fårö, Stora and Lilla Karlsö and Heligholm in the deepest south of Gotland. Plants and animals dominate his diary, but also architecture, manners and customs and the prehistoric remains dotting the landscape.

On his return home, Linnæus presented a report to his commissioners, accounted for his results to the Royal Academy of Sciences and, as newly appointed professor at Uppsala, delivered his introductory lecture on the necessity of journeys of exploration in one's own country. The diary was edited and published as a travel account in 1745. The printed version of the journey is, compared to the diary, drier and more concise in its narrative, poorer in personal details and incidents. Many, but not all, of his drawings are to be found in the printed version, albeit somewhat improved. Attached to the printed version is a map of Gotland by the surveyor Jacob Faggot.

The diary is kept at the Linnean Society at Burlington House, London, which I visited and where I photographed the entire diary as well as some illustrations by Linnæus's own hand that have never been published before.

During the summers of 2005 and 2006 I travelled around in Linnæus's footsteps, visiting the same places on the very days when Linnæus was there in 1741, trying to see what Linnæus had seen, or what is there today but was not there then.

This has turned into a new travel diary with photographs of landscapes and observations of plants and habitation which still exist, notes on what has disappeared and what has been added. Many of the plant habitats, rare to Linnæus, with rarities which he had not seen in the wild before, are still there in the same places. Soil conditions are often unchanged. But novelties have arrived: the large Mästermyr marsh has been drained, and mile-long sugar beet fields shine where Linnæus saw sedge and marshy pools. On the windswept, barren Näsudden headland, the wind turbines stand in line. But along the winding road past Burs church the wild pear still thrives, the very one Linnæus and his students saw.

The diary text, written by both Linnæus himself and by several of his party as dictated by him, is in parts difficult to read, particularly where the writing on the pages is thin and faint. Of great help to me here has been Bertil Gullander's book, *Linné på Gotland* (1971) with extracts from the diary and the printed version of the travel account. The spelling has been somewhat modernised while his manner of expressing himself is that of the era.

Together with Helga Jonsson, I have photographed the Gotland landscape on the days Linnæus was there. It has become a book with Linnæus's diary text day by day and a text about what the visitor sees today, amply illustrated.

My visit to London and Burlington House was made possible by financial support from the association De badande Wännerna i Visby. Grants from the foundation Stiftelsen Riksbankens jubileumsfond, and Länsförsäkringar Gotland have enabled the printing.

My particular gratitude goes to Allan Larsson who gave me the idea for the book and who has supported me along the way.

In 2005 and 2006 I was able to discuss ideas and design at two Linnæus symposia at Naturum, Vamlingbo rectory. The jubilee year steering committee of the regional museum of Gotland participated in the production of the book. Thanks also go to the Linnæus Secretariat of the Royal Academy of Sciences, its Secretary General Åse Berglund and the co-ordinator of the Linnæus gardens Birgitta Sandström Lagerkrantz and to the members of the reference group of the Kronoberg region with whom I have worked closely on recreating the home of Linnæus's birth and gardens at Råhult and with whom I have been able to discuss Linnean matters along the way. Finally, librarian and archivist Gina Douglas of the Linnean Society has been of invaluable help to me.

Sundre, September 2007

Marita Jonsson

The publication of the English translation is done in association with the Linnean Society, London.

The famous portrait of Linnæus after his Lapland journey.

22 JUNE (3 JULY) *We awoke with daylight at two o'clock in the morning and had in front of our eyes the Carlsö islands. The weather gradually calmed and the ship glided forward slowly. The Carlsö islands appeared ever steeper and taller all around like ramparts. The sea was as smooth as glass with velvet scoters swimming here and there. No porpoises, or dolphins, nor ships were seen. The seamen whiled away the time telling tales about two large carbuncles said to have been in the church of St Clement's in Wisby which sank to the bottom when the Danish King Waldemar IV's ship was wrecked. They alone believed that the mast could still be seen in calm water and that in the sun the glitter of the carbuncles lit up the eyes of seafarers.*

Gotland gradually came into sight, Klinta hill became ever clearer. Passing the Carlsö islands on our right, we finally left their shores on the same side, which were quite steeply hewn off as though built up to a considerable height with limestone and mortar. The sun shone warmly and time sped by with the day until two o'clock in the afternoon when we stepped ashore in Wisby harbour.

No sooner had we entered the town when captains, lieutenants, barons and assessors greeted our arrival and the people showed themselves to be kind and friendly (…) I was given lodgings with the wife of Inspector Lundmark (who was an ornament to her sex), (Carl Lundmark 1701–1761, married to Anna Catharina Krohn 1716–1792, daughter of tenant farmer Jochim Krohn at Vibble Farm) who received me, treated me as if I had been a prince or a son of the gods.

Sketch of Visby town wall from the diary.

3 July

In the first week of July, Carl Linnæus arrived in Gotland with six young travellers. The party had left the island of Öland where their journey had been very successful, but they were a week late, and Carl was worried that all the plants he had heard about would have finished flowering. It was with great excitement that they watched Gotland emerge, the large legendary island in the Baltic Sea, full of history and relics from the Viking era and the Middle Ages and with a somewhat different flora from the rest of the country. Their expectations were great but their impatience can be read between the lines. He genuinely yearned to set foot on land and begin a new important journey of exploration.

Legend met them already at sea. As they passed the Karlsö islands, Valdemar Atterdag was brought back to life. His invasion in 1361 was still fresh in the minds of the seafarers. Gotland had been conquered and a ransom had been exacted, the Danish army had left the island with the riches the men of Gotland had accumulated from successful raiding expeditions in the East and from trading under the name of the Hanseatic League. In the town square the burgers of Visby had been forced to fill three ale-vats with silver. The Danes had then sailed away with the treasure but had also grasped the opportunity to steal the two magnificent carbuncles from the tower of the Mary Church (alternatively St Nicholas's or St Clement's). Carbuncle was the name of a ruby-red stone, which shines in the dark, and "every night", according to the chronicler Strelow, "24 watchmen guarded the

church so that nobody could pass through there after sunset without risking his life". In legend no robber ever gets away with his booty. Neither did Valdemar. His war fleet was struck by a terrible storm, and outside Stora Karlsö island the ship sank. And now the men on Linnæus's ship testified, as had so many fishermen on the island, that they had seen the treasure glimmer on the sea bottom.

Coming by ferry from Oskarshamn and arriving at Visby, you will see the same beautiful sight as Carl and his friends. Two islands, Stora and Lilla Karlsö [big and little K.], rising out of the water like a mirage, two high plateaus with precipitous peaks and steep slopes which, on closer inspection, reveal deep cave formations in the hillsides, and seabirds living on shelves in the cliffs flying around by the thousand. Then the enormous silhouette of Gotland's west coast with Högklint to the south of Visby, a wall of mountain, 48 meters above sea level, stretching north seemingly into eternity, a rugged and bare landscape, shaped like an invincible fortress raised by Nature itself. Finally, the artificial harbour, the ferry destination, the reef and the old entrance with Kruttornet [Gunpowder Tower], the defence work from the 12th century, resembling an unassailable monolith of limestone, and the encircling town wall with towers and turrets around the medieval town of Visby with its tall storehouse gables and church ruins; in truth a legendary Vineta, the Baltic town said to have disappeared into the sea.

"The weather gradually calmed and the ship glided forward slowly."
Left: Kruttornet [Gunpowder Tower], the 12th century defence tower at the entrance of Visby harbour.
Overleaf: The old Pharmacy, Visby. The town wall with knights from Valdemar Atterdag's army during the Medieval Week on Gotland.

23 JUNE (4 JULY) *In the morning we walked to view the town, taking up the entire day, for here we thought ourselves seeing Romam in nuce (Rome in a nutshell). So many, such splendid and magnificent churches were to be found all over the town, turned to ruins by time and changes of government, 'headless' and roofless. The tall walls of large dressed stone without bricks, the magnificent pillars and artful vaults turned our thoughts to times gone by, to the former splendour of this town now completely dilapidated, but then again, considering the competition for this town between Swedes, Danes and Germans, even more solid buildings could have been knocked down, for what can withstand the fire of war?*

The town was situated on the left side of the land which extended within a semi-circle up the side of the hill, not large, surrounded and enclosed by a high wall with several sturdy towers in ancient fashion with double ramparts, albeit in ruins. The streets were uneven, narrow and cramped. The alleys were totally irregular, the houses German, some of stone, some half-timbered, some of wood. The roofs were mostly tiled, though bought from Germany.

The water was clear, plentiful, often running so that even in the cellars there were frequently fishponds.

The people spoke almost Norwegian with a Danish accent. Tried hard to be well-mannered.

Cicuta major, Echium majus, Cichorium, Chenopodium folio absolete triangulo upsaliense, Anthriscus, Nasturtium oelandicum, Bursa pas-

4 July

Medieval Visby with its town wall, towers and turrets. View from Almedalen.

"Rome in a nutshell" Carl thought on waking and walking out on his very first day in Visby.

He was amazed by the "splendid" and "magnificent" churches which were now in ruins, he noted the pillars and the vaults and the high walls, he walked the "uneven, narrow and crowded streets and irregular alleys". He looked at the houses – German, he thought – of stone, half-timbered or of wood, mostly "ancient, whose stones and walls were wholly blackened by age" and which still had their medieval vaults extant. Most of the houses, he noted, had vaults on the ground floor and there were some which also had vaults on the top floor.

He described the shape of the town, "semi-circular landwards, up the hillside" with a high surrounding wall with towers and double ramparts.

In the cathedral were some gigantic bones which the group saw were from a whale and the remains of the "judgement day fish" although most of it had already been "eaten away".

Visby is likely to have been in a more ruinous state when Linnæus arrived than ever before or since. The island had become Swedish with the peace treaty of Brömsebro in 1645 after nearly 300 years of Danish rule. Some decades later, however, new battles began with Denmark, and when the Danes finally left the island for good they took the opportunity to blast to pieces the palace of Visborg. In the 1720s there were only 1,186 people registered in the town. The churches stood in ruins, as did many of the old storehouses. Both King

Medieval house gables in St Hansgatan street.
Below: Viper's bugloss.

toris folio and Hyoseris minima (hemlock, viper's bugloss, chicory, oak-leaved goosefoot, cow parsley, hutchinsia, shepherd's purse, lamb's succory), not previously seen in Sweden, were to be found in the streets and by the churches.

The large bones kept in the cathedral were whalebones. The fish hanging above St George in the same church was mostly eaten away (…) credulum vulgus (the credulous people) believe that once it is completely destroyed the day of judgement will come. Not far off then!

Immediately outside the town to the east, outside the eastern toll-gate, a large stone cross was to be seen, the circle of which was adorned with letters although now overgrown with moss (…)

The houses in the town itself were mostly ancient, the stone and walls already wholly blackened by age. In most of the inhabited houses, built of solid stone, the lower rooms were vaulted, it was also said that all these rooms had earlier been storehouses for merchants, houses were indeed found where even the upper floors were vaulted.

The water was said not to cause stones [gall or kidney] despite being only calcareum as the ground where everything grew, apart from the top-soil, was limestone (…)

The day was beautiful and clear.

Karl X Gustaf and King Karl XII had had plans to move Visby to Slite for the sake of a better harbour. Suggestions to sell and demolish the ruins had been put forward by the government which saw them as huge caches of ready dressed stone that could be used for new buildings.

Memorial cross at Korsbetningen over the battle against the Danes on 27 July 1361.

Linnæus arrived just before Visby entered a new era of prosperity. Commerce and industry were given a real impetus in the late 1700s, the population quadrupled, and the area between the present-day streets Adelsgatan and Södra murgatan was divided into new plots.

After Visby was designated as a World Heritage Site in 1995, much has happened to the inner part of the town. The government has shouldered responsibility for the upkeep and for guaranteeing that the maintenance will be done in accordance with international agreements. Everything has been documented, and about 200 houses have been listed as of historic interest, each one with its own restoration plan. Houses have been restored, modern materials from the 1960s, such as cement and plastic paint, have been removed, making room for traditional materials and methods which age along with the houses. But opinions differ among antiquarians, architects and house owners. The old collides with demands for financial return and modern administration. The gutted interiors of the 1960s and '70s are undoubtedly more profitable in terms of conventional calculations. The antiquarians also differ. Are not the '60s reconstructions part of the history of the old houses, similar to annual rings in a tree? The antiquarians argue that most houses can cope with alterations, provided they start from the soul of the building. Often it is the individual property owner who is the most zealous conservator.

The streets Strandgatan, Mellangatan and St Hansgatan show well-renovated medieval storehouses with limewashed walls and woodwork painted with linseed oil-based linseed paints. Modernisations of the last fifty years have often been peeled off to reveal the original features of the houses. Simple and functional is how the storehouses of the Middle Ages appear, and it may at times be difficult to understand that they have stood the test of time for more than 700 years.

The moats outside the walls form a well-kept lawn, though somewhat scorched by the sun, in a parkland of wild roses and apple trees. Like Carl and his group, I take a walk to the Korsbetning and a look at the cross raised there; on 27 July 1361 a decisive battle took place here between the Gotlanders and the troops of the Danish King Valdemar Atterdag. The Gotland peasant army was ill equipped; 2,000 men died on the battlefield and were buried where the cross is raised, close to what was once Solberga monastery.

23

Left: In St Hansgatan the medieval houses stand gable by gable.
Below: Kilgränd lane.

24 JUNE (5 JULY) *On Midsummer's Day we were in the cathedral. After the service we walked around in the town towards the northern wall. What beautiful fields, whence flowering ears of rye now produced an agreeable smell. In the fields grew genuine chervil, Cerefolium sativum, which is sown commonly in gardens all over Sweden, and that in abundance, also Cynapium (fool's parsley), for which anyone wishing to collect chervil for kitchen and cordial-making in the spring has to look out in order to save people from going mad and crazy.*

There was also Chaerophyllum geniculis tumutibus (rough chervil) here. Some had built themselves leaf huts, most people had decked their houses with oak leaves, of which we had seen whole wagon loads pulled by horses brought in the day before, birch leaves being banned (…)

On our way to church we saw graves in the churchyard strewn with every kind of flower, though not all but only the gravestones under which people rested whose kinsfolk were still alive. The same is said to happen at every feast day, but in the winter only spruce branches [are used].

The populace ran riot in the street. Farm servants and maids ran laughing all night long to their playgrounds.

The stoves in this town were made of iron, all from Norway. In the houses one saw in many places pictures of the king and queen, printed and coloured, put up on the walls, particularly outside the town among the peasants (…)

In the local people's houses there were benches in the rooms covered with either long, or many small square, cushions ut molliter ossa cubent (for the bones to rest softly).

The tower of the cathedral and in the foreground medieval warehouses.

5 July

Carl and his friends took part in the midsummer celebrations in Visby and rejoiced at seeing the houses decked with oak leaves and flowers. Then as now, the young turned night into day and "ran laughing all night long to their playgrounds".

According to our modern way of calculating time, the party only arrived here in early July. Therefore, when I visit Visby it is already the month of July, and midsummer celebrations are but a memory.

I pay a visit to the cathedral and realise that the environment must have been different in 1741. At that time the church was surrounded by a high wall with narrow entrances, shaped like stepped gables, still standing like monoliths, which were the gateways into to the church-yard. The leaning gravestones by the hillside would have been placed on the ground.

The exterior of the church itself has also been altered. The present three baroque 'hoods' did not exist, there was one 'hood' to the west, and to the east two tall spires. An inspection report from 1701 points out a number of faults; the roof of grooved 'monk' tiles is so poor that the tiles are falling off, the mortar joints have come adrift from the stone walls, the rendering is gone, the cordons around the tower are so rotten that they can be picked off, and it is ages since the spires on the towers have been treated with tar.

Improvements are likely to have been carried out after that, but the tower 'hood' and the spires were replaced shortly after Linnæus's visit.

Linnæus noticed the iron stoves in the homes of the Visby burgers. They were small, neat, square stoves on legs with relief motifs on all sides. Such a stove can be found in the Burmeister house in Strandgatan, a small museum showing the home of a merchant family from the period 1650–1750. When in the mid 1600s the island became Swedish, Gotland was granted its first Swedish regional governor. He was to live in Strandgatan in a two-storey house built of timber, dovetailed at the corners, a method of construction alien to the island. Interior walls and ceilings were decorated by a German immigrant artist, Johan Bartsch Senior. One can imagine that building in that style became fashionable. One of the merchants of the town, Hans Burmeister, newly arrived from Lübeck, had a similar house built nearby and there too it was the same artist who was responsible for the interior décor. Both buildings, the Old Residence and the Burmeister house, fine examples of baroque interior décor, are administered by the regional museum, and it is possible to borrow a key for a visit.

I enter the Burmeister house. The door is divided into two, the lower part can be locked, and the upper part used as an open window, – practical on a hot day like this. The interior is cool and still in contrast to the intense surge of summer life in restaurants and cafés along the Strandgatan. The stairwell is painted in putty white with vigorous yellow acanthus arabesques. On one of the door halves a buxom woman is portrayed, carrying a dish filled with meat. Maybe it is the lady of the house receiving us? The living room is in darkness; a pale light streaks in through the painted leaded windows. The walls show Bible stories and sayings in German. Between the ceiling beams there is a throng of figures. "Horror vacui", I think, the artist has made use of every single centimetre. The cabinet nearby shows hunting scenes and greenery. I would like to think that Carl was invited to a home like this during his visit to Visby.

Left: The Burmeister house, the drawing room with its sandstone fireplace and walls painted with Biblical motifs and ribbons of text from the 17th century.

Below: "One saw here in a vaulted chamber a fine bath house stove, resembling a tiled stove. The fire was put in below the vault of stones b, when the damper c, was closed to make the smoke pass through d, e to f outside the wall. Once the fire had burnt out, the damper was closed at d, and opened at c, to make the heat from the stones pass into the chambers and particularly when water was poured thereupon causing vapor calidus (hot steam) fotus (to refresh) the room."

27

A boat of the type that Linnæus saw by one of the remaining marshes along the west coast north of Visby.

"…and the boat completely flat, made entirely of boards…"

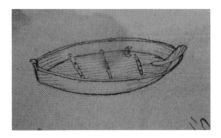

Junius 25.

25 JUNE (6 JULY) *Although we had already ordered horses yesterday evening for nine o'clock today we did not get them until the afternoon, and only then after having called on assistance from the deputy mayor; a sign of a cumbersome economy in the town.*

We did, however, have the opportunity to make notes on some seabirds.

This day was very warm, as was yesterday. Our journey took us north and along the western shore. On the way we saw Bellis officinarum (daisy), growing plentifully although it has otherwise only been observed on the plains of Scania.

Orchis hiante cucullo, Orchis minima albid; Lotus tetragonolobus by the shore. Rubia cynanchica grew everywhere in the wood, quite low with white flowers, like Aparine minima on Öland island. Grossularia spinosa, Rosa, Crataegus spinosa, Asclepias, Prunus sylvestris (military orchid, burnt orchid, dragon's teeth, madder, fen bedstraw, gooseberries, dogrose, hawthorn, spleenwort and blackthorn). Helianthemum (rockrose) and wires of alpine bearberry along with cowberry, juniper bushes and pines covered the ground entirely; but heather and spruce absented themselves from these dry areas where twin flowers were also to be seen from time to time. Many fields stood yellow with wild turnip and meadows with Ranunculo acri (meadow buttercup). Chervil grew in the fields, Trifolium lupulinum on the ground, Cotoneaster on the hills. Jasione here and there (hop trefoil, wild cotoneaster, sheep's bit).

After one fjärdingsväg we arrived at Korpeklint, said to be the highest hill in the area, where we found plenty of petrificata in the quarries, for all the way from the shore to here we had been travelling below the

6 July

Cave opening at Lummelunda.

Visby in July is an alien place to those who live on the island all year round. The first week of July is when the summer people arrive, the population of the town doubles, restaurants and shops open up in the most unlikely places, and the rhythm of the small town, with people going to work and school at around eight o'clock and turning their lights out at eleven, is disrupted as the town is transformed into a town of youth that never sleeps.

In the crowded grocer's shop by the square I have difficulty finding groceries for the day's outing and almost wish that Linnæus's mayor could have made way for me and hastened the queue at the check-out.

The bridle path Linnæus took is now a one-way road for cars, turning into an asphalt walk along the seashore to the Snäckgärdsbaden bathing-place. Immediately north of the town wall there are three moats running parallel, their sides partially built up with mortar, where butterbur grows with its large rhubarb-like leaves. Shingle and sand alternate along the shore. In one place a heap of small "button corals", minute corals of the now extinct family Paleocyclus, have collected, reminding me of the little cloth buttons of my childhood. In the warm summer weather the beaches are full of bathers, and I look longingly at the inviting waves. But there is no time for swimming. Instead I follow in Linnæus's footsteps and find my way up the steep slope to the main road towards Lummelunda.

Carl and his companions looked at a stream that had its beginning

Below: A sedge marsh.
Overleaf: Lummelunda iron works with mill and watercourse, edged with ramsons and ground elder.

ridge which runs towards the headland in the north like the bluff on Öland, but on the west side towards the sea, it is wholly broken up into overhangs like 'death leaps' with the upper part of the side jutting out further than the other [lower one]. This quarry is of pure limestone which splinters somewhat horizontally. It looks grey but, when broken off, it is generally completely white like quartz and almost translucent without palpable grains like marble.

From Korpeklint we travelled on top of this ridge. All the way it was so bright that it hurt our eyes, since all the soil was full of lime; lime comes from clay, crumbles in the air, whitens, disintegrates to form lime-soil (…)

(…) Five fjärdingsväg from the town we arrived at Öfwersteqvarn in the parish of Lummelund, where a blast furnace and a hammer had once stood. We viewed the wondrous stream which has its beginning at Martebo marsh and from there stretches for one fjärdingsväg below hills and valleys, emerging here where the bluff is broken off towards the western side at its base as though from a small vault, two fathoms wide and one fathom high. Below the lime-hill where the stream immediately forms a fall for the mill, the saw and the hammer, so high that it is among the most significant in Sweden. Here were opportunities to establish installations of far greater importance, if 'Gotland Manufacturers' were ever to come into existence…

After travelling six fjärdingsväg from the town we arrived at the Nygranne inn, having passed Lummelund church. Shortly thereafter we found growing in the meadows a plant, never before observed in Sweden and very abundant, Moly paeticum, called rams *locally (…) People told us that wherever it grows it drives away other plants, proof of which we also saw everywhere around it; for that reason it was sown in hop yards to banish cow parsley. Cattle are said to eat it happily, but it makes the milk and the butter stink of garlic. This bulb has precisely the same vigour and effect as Victoralis rotunda ('victory garlic') from the apothecaries' stores and ought to be used in its place.*

Lummelund church had hardly disappeared out of our sight when on the left hand side we saw a large marshland, with a diameter of more than several gun shots which was called the church-mire where a grass grew everywhere like a cereal in a cultivated field without any other plant, it was one and a half ells tall, called great fen-sedge (…) People thatch their barn roofs with it, for between midsummer and the feast of St Olaf [29 July], it is cut down with scythes, is placed together in bund-

"Helianthemum (rockrose) … covered the ground entirely."

at Martebo marsh and ran below hills and valleys to Överstekvarn where it emerged out of a vault. Nowadays the fissure is part of the Lummelunda caves, one of the island's greatest attractions, and it is now known that the cave-halls stretch kilometre after kilometre into the bedrock due to water having seeped through swallow holes in Martebo marsh and run along horizontal layers in the bedrock towards the sea. The caves were discovered in the 1950s by three schoolboys and are now open to visitors. These days in the summer, there are endless queues of curious tourists waiting to see the caves and the variously coloured stalactites hanging from the roof and upright stalagmites on the walls. Tunnels have been constructed to enable tourists to be escorted in and out of the caves.

Lummelunda iron works were closed already in Linnæus's time. But an enormous mill wheel can still be visited, and I am prepared to agree with him that it is one of the most significant ones in Sweden. Along the water there are withered leaves of ramsons among the ground elder, and the smell of garlic lingers heavily under the thirty metre tall deciduous trees covered in climbing ivy. It is a magical place for wandering around on a day when the blisteringly hot sun scorches the limestone roads, turning the landscape grey with dust. Here in the penumbra it is cool and damp. I see a kingfisher by the water, and up in the foliage the songbirds make music.

Before turning inland at Lummelunda church, I pass Tjaul farm with about one hundred white beef cattle grazing in the sun and, as a sign of our modern energy provision, a number of wind turbines in a line against the horizon. They stand still in the summer heat. The surrounding areas are different from the ones Linnæus saw. The marsh has been drained, and the church mere with its fen sedge is gone. I enter the church, one of the many Romanesque buildings of the island with a nave of classical Gotland measurements, 10 ells wide and 15 ells long. Rebuilding was begun in the 14th century but only the chancel was completed. The murals show pictures from the Roman era as well as from the 15th century.

In the 17th century, Lummelunda iron works were operated by its proprietor Christoffer Neuman. The church bears numerous traces of that, conferring on it a sense of being in part the church of the iron works. Family graves are in the floor of the chancel. The bronze chan-

Medieval servant woman with a sack and flagon from the capital abacus of the south portal, Martebo church.

les, not dried, regardless of which end sticks out, and thus roofs became better, tighter and more durable than with straw. Those who do not have any of their own buy the right to harvest it where it grows, for between eight and sixteen stivers per horse drawn wagon load. This had never been seen before by us in, or beyond, Sweden. (…)

Think of all the wholly sterile, useless marshes in Sweden where this could be sown and bear fruit. (…)

In the meadow there was an Orchis we had not seen before, three quarters [of an ell] high, had more than 20 flowers, of structura corollarum (the appearance of the flower), one can see that this Orchis is a morio (green-winged orchid) although it is externally as different as night is from day, both in its prolificness and colour of the flower. People here called all orchids 'St John's keys'.

In this place the 'gates' [openings in the fences] were constructed leje smolandorum (in the manner of the province of Småland), but hewn into one of the posts and inserted into the other, against which stood a board, hanging on hooks to prevent the cross-pieces from falling out of where they were inserted before the board was removed.

Before we arrived at Martebo church there was on the right hand side in the wood a mere or small lake. It was both wide and long, but far from deep, one could almost walk across it without drowning, had it not been for the mud here and there on the bottom, although everywhere else there was sand. Straight across it we saw some large green tussocks, wanted to know what kind of plant it was that stood so green and tussocky. We found a couple of boats by the shore, but one has to believe that the crafts here were in proportion to the waters. The boat was five ells long, one and a half ells wide in the middle, one and a half quarter ells deep, looked like a box with points at both ends, in formam ovali lanceolatum (oval shaped). Both ends were perpendicular, as were the boards, and the boat completely flat, made entirely of boards. Neither oars nor rudder were used, only a large pole with which one set out to sea on this terrifying lake.

The main houses in this area have roofs generally covered with boards, lying from the ridge of the roof to the eave without any birch bark or turf underneath. (…)

At eight o'clock in the evening we arrived at the Martebo rectory where we stayed overnight with the Reverend Mr Sven Follin (1680–1745) and his son Mr Petrus Westphal (1708–1769), having travelled one and a half fjärdingsväg from the inn.

deliers were donated by the Neuman family. The altarpiece, the pulpit and the pews were designed by the artist Johan Bartsch.

The road meanders across the drained marsh towards Martebo. The ground is infertile and difficult to cultivate, the plant cover sparse. Draining marshes did not always result in improved soil. Single pine trees stand among the reeds. A small road leads to the dam, Landträsk. This was once one of the island's biggest lakes. It was drained in the mid 1800s along with the marsh. On the bottom of the former lake an artificial irrigation dam was built in the 1970s for the benefit of the surrounding farms. About fifteen species of birds breed here. I climb up on to the grassy bank and see a few tufted duck, coot and Slavonian grebe swimming among the reeds and water lilies.

The church at Martebo is one of the most magnificent on the island. With its three imposing, stone sculpted portals, probably by the anonymous master Egypticus, who was also active in the south of the island, this is a large church, erected during the height of the Gothic period in the middle of the 14th century. The abacuses on the capitals of the portals tell of the Annunciation, of Mary and Elizabeth, the Birth of Christ, the Adoration of the Magi up to the Crucifixion and Laying in the Tomb. But the people depicted are the peasant men and women of Medieval Gotland, dressed in their everyday apparel and with the artefacts they would have used in their everyday lives.

The farmhouses seem to be from a later date, and I do not think there are any houses left here of the ones Linnæus would have seen. After some searching I do at least find a wing of a building with a so-called fall-board roof, that is, a roof with the boards running from ridge to eave.

Martebo. A small limestone wing with a fallboard roof, so-called *faltak*.

26 JUNE (7 JULY) *As soon as we had risen in the morning we walked out into the meadows to see what curiosities nature would have to offer there. In the street as well as in the fields there grew Anagallis flore rubro (scarlet pimpernel) which until then had only been found on the plain of Scania near the town of Lund. Ranunculus erectus ecinatus (corn buttercup) made the fields yellow close to the ground. Ballota, Ophioglossum (adder's-tongue) from which a healing salve is made locally (…)*

People commonly used only two kinds for dyeing: 'goat bark' which is Rhamnus catharticus (buckthorn) and 'yellow bark' which is Frangula (alder buckthorn). The bark is dried, macerated in weak lye or in lye and water, then boiled in lye, which produces a yellow dye. Radices valerianae (roots of common valerian) are used here locally in passione hysterica (for hysteria), and for erysipelas they use sulphur and pepper, for the ague gunpowder, snuff, schnapps and tobacco mixed, which in cases where they do not cause vomitum (vomiting) they are expedited with lukewarm water (…)

From there we travelled towards Stenkyrka, the shortcut through the forest. Along the way we saw an old tar stack burning. The wood for burning tar was nothing but old pine stumps dug out of the ground. Such stumps, it was said, could only come from old and mature trees which do not decompose fully in the ground, but the longer they remain there the better they become, so that a stump that had not been in the ground for 30 years, since being cut down, is said not to have absorbed enough resin, something which nevertheless seems to strive contra leges vegetationes (against the laws of vegetation).

The tower of Stenkyrka church was erected in the late 1300s.

7 July

Martebo meadow by the church is made up of hazel. The meadow flora of old seems to have disappeared. The road towards Stenkyrka is asphalt and passes still today through a wood of deciduous trees. With surprise, I note all the birch. The rye in a small field looks fine, the summer drought has not been too severe here. Then I understand the context; Linnæus noted it already in his journal. This is clay soil.

Stenkyrka church has become a 'wayfarer church', and at this time of year, coffee is served next to the rectory. Signs at the crossroads reflect changed times: "Mix Ranch", "Frisör" [Barber] and "Bilverk-stad" [Garage] are evidently to be found here. I see no tar stack, but there are still local heritage societies on the island that burn tar in the traditional manner.

When Linnæus toured the area a tar company had acquired the monopoly of the tar trade. Tar was one of Gotland's most important exports and the light-coloured tar was highly praised. The peasants sold tar by the barrel in the rural harbours to foreign buyers. When the island became Swedish in 1645 the rulers of Sweden, then a Great Power, saw fit to ban free trade, and it was the most dynamic of the entrepreneurs who also were to monopolise the tar trade, Christoffer Neumann, proprietor of the iron works at Lummelunda, being one of them.

I pass some stone houses with tiled roofs at Sorby. One of them looks as if it might have been built at the beginning of the 18th century. Maybe Linnæus's party saw it as he wrote in his journal: "At

Below: Mustard.
Bottom: Tar stack and tar wood.
Right: "At some farmsteads one saw …
the gables usually timbered."

The ground and the fields in the area were full of clay. Here they sowed wheat, rye and barley, but not oats, flax or hemp or peas. We understood that the people were only little accustomed to handling flax. Fucus (seaweed) is used for fertilising the fields here as well, although the soil is mixed with clay. It fertilises the soil but does not remain rich for as long as [with] dung. The crops are sown for two years, the third year is for rest, fertilised again, rye is sown, second [year] barley without fertiliser.

At some farmsteads one saw stone houses with tiled roofs although the upper floor or the gable was usually timbered. The walls were of limestone, and said to have been built with mortar of bleke [carbonated lime] and sand.

*

In this area people use neither tiled stoves nor dampers for their stoves but most of them have a focum perennum (permanent fire).

On the marshes where the sedge had been cut down the previous summer, one saw the area still standing bare, nothing had as yet grown in, for it was said that once the same grass had been harvested, it will take a few years before it regains its normal growth (…) By one farm one saw

Linnæus described and drew pictures of how the Gotlanders raise their wooden fences, *bandtun*, with upright poles and diagonally placed boards tied together with withes (see next page). The tradition lives on.

that a fair amount of mustard had been sown and was flowering happily.

Sedum petraeum foliis basi leberis (reflexed stonecrop). This Sedum has not been observed in Sweden before, but has been accurately described and depicted by Dillenius in England.

From Stenkyrka onwards, limestone began to be more and more plentiful which was noted by the fact that it lay white on the roads, for it whitens as soon as it is worn, but not so the grey stone. One did indeed see whole areas of land white with pure limestone, lying bare with no soil, flat and no higher than the surrounding soil. Where these bare lime fields were somewhat lower at the edges, one saw something resembling a dried-out marsh, but with white soil, called bleke, not only in one place but in many. Hence one took the opportunity to examine whether this bleke, (from which can be concluded absolutely that it is a terra calcaria non vero cretacera (a lime gravel)) is either the mother or the daughter of limestone.

At the greatest risk for our lives, we travelled across these white lime fields, across which the road stretched quite bare, and which nothing could improve; the horses stumbled as though on slippery ice and got no foothold, for the lime has the property that the more it is worn, albeit unevenly, the smoother it becomes.

At Ire there was a small stream, now dried out, running across the road. There we alighted to see what nature might play in the dried out riverbed. Here one found a small Caucalis (a kind of chervil), which regrettably had not yet opened its umbella (flower) (…) On all the rough fields, which are more than plentiful here in the forest, one saw such a large quantity of Arbuto repente (bearberry) that it would be sufficient for all the manufacture in Sweden. Thus, no need for it to be ordered from other places, for in the whole of Sweden there is not such a large quantity to be found as the one which we have seen today and yesterday.

In the evening at five o'clock we arrived at Hangvar rectory where we were given lodging with the pastorem loci Mr Hansten (Samuel Andersson Hansten 1702–1767) who with his wife was absent, each at a different place. We therefore had to install ourselves which, after they had been informed of our errand, did not appear so singular to them as, on their return home, seeing so many strangers which seemed rare; we could not fail to observe that, on noticing this, our host at first gave us a hard look.

This whole day ended with the setting of the sun in a cloud. The entire journey today was nearly three miles.

some farmsteads one saw stone houses with tiled roofs…"

The tradition of building wooden fences using upright poles with diagonal boards in between, tied together with withes, is kept alive. Old poles are successively replaced in the traditional manner, and in places new fences are built using old techniques.

Linnæus travelled across white lime fields where the lime rock was exposed, and where the horses slipped as though on ice. Nowadays the road is gravelled but in the summer it shines white with lime dust just as in the 18th century.

By the Ihre river he mentions plants such as chervil, marsh pennywort, blue fleabane, white water lily and lungwort. They grow here still. And the branched St Bernard's lily still flowers prolifically by the roadsides north of the church. The hawthorn butterfly which he noted is so numerous that I feel as though I were part of Linnæus's party. Only, I have lagged behind a little…

He does not mention the Elinghem derelict church, but he must have passed by it. It is beautifully situated in a meadow surrounded by a wide circular wall, possibly the remains of an ancient fort from prehistoric times. The last incumbent here was Rasmus Rodeus who died in 1617. Maybe the church had been abandoned after a fire? The nave and chancel from the 12th century are now in ruins, the vaults have collapsed, as have parts of the walls. But it is a beautiful place where services and concerts are still held in the summer.

In the evening I arrive at Hangvar.

A small road where limestone rocks and gravel show through.
Below: Elinghem derelict church.

43

27 JUNE (8 JULY) *In the morning we were up at four o'clock to make drawings of four runic stones which lay close to each other in the church-yard; they were complete, particularly two, very much worn, but with work and diligence the following words could be read (…)*

(…) By the church wall there grew a large Fraxinus whose even thallus was slit open perpendicularly on three sides, somewhat at a slant, from the root as far up as one could see (…). It was said that lightning had once struck this tree, as far as old peasants remembered.

The fields were full of lime gravel. This gravel was said to cool the fields in strong heat.

Everywhere by the farmsteads one could see baking ovens outside the walls, only the 'mine' or entrance to the oven was inside the house, with a loose cover over the oven itself, thus the oven did not take up any space inside the house.

Very little alder was said to grow in this place; and we have not seen it in more than two places, and not much there.

Wild mustard grew here abundantly among the barley but extraordinarily enough not among the rye (…)

The corn is not tossed here after it has been thrashed but is only aired in the hayloft; as the wind blows through the door so the chaff blows away.

Seals are captured here on the seashore with lying nets or upstanding nets. The upstanding nets are erected in the shape of a crescent beyond the stones, for the seal is always said to keep to his usual stone, always climbing up on to it from the inner side, the landward side, always with

8 July

It is early morning at Hangvar. The cranes are quietly feeding in the early sun. The coastal parish has plenty of marshland and the coast, which is wild and wrathful with steep peaks, is a nature reserve.

The four rune stones which Carl interpreted are no longer in the churchyard: one is kept in the tower room of Hangvar church, the others were probably incorporated into the chancel floor when some restoration work was done. Now they are to be found underneath the large floor carpet.

The ash that had been struck by lightning is gone. A new special tree, a chestnut, has grown to considerable dimensions and stands to the south not far from the entrance door of the church.

I was offered a lemon drink at Suderby farm and looked at one of the many protruding, roofed baking ovens which still exist in the area. The farm is situated on a small rise of flat rock south of the church. It is a large 18th century stone house, built as the residence of the head of the county constabulary. For fifty years it was a rectory.

A meandering forest road leads to Kappelshamn. Barley still grows in the shingle fields, but the mustard which Carl and his friends noted is noticeably absent. The deep inlet is still a safe harbour where the fishing boats jostle at the concrete pier. Further out in the bay, I see large barges on their way to the crusher at Storugns to collect limestone. Strandridargården [the house of the mounted customs inspector] has ceased to be an inn, now it is the Maven (Gulls) at the pier that caters for hungry tourists.

Chestnut at Hangvar church.
Below: Protruding baking oven with roof. Suderby farm, Hangvar.

45

Limestone kiln at Kappelshamn.
Illustration by Linnæus.

its nose facing the sea, and as soon as it gets a fright it runs into the net. The lying net is laid out like a square fence around stones and right down on the ground, but with ropes stretching up on land and, when these are pulled, the upper part of a pole rises at the water's edge whereupon, as soon as it has got on to its stone and the people crept to the shore to reach the ropes, the seal is ensnared in the net and killed.

Flounder is there in fair quantity, [caught] by angling or trotline, also called 'eel line'. The bait for this is Baltic herring cut into pieces.

The reason why there was fen sedge in the beds instead of straw is said to be because in the winter the straw had been given to the cattle; the maid who is to make such a bed must not have weak, tender fingers, so-called milk fingers.

On our way from here we saw along the way several limestone quarries. They were no deeper than the Ölanders' quarries at Alvaret, at the most two ells deep. The limestone was horizontalis, somewhat fissilis (split), light grey but at the break itself, or in the cracks, a little ferrugineus (rust coloured).

After three fjärdingsväg we arrived at Capelshamn where we saw a large sea bay extending far inland, making a beautiful harbour for mariners. It was secure in all weathers, except from the north-north-west, the only wind that could attack it. On its west side there was a limestone-kiln by the shore.

We were entertained to dinner by the mounted customs officer Hans Kiörsner. We walked along the shore to gather petrificata and corals, among them very many conchitae striatae (grooved bivalves) and a particularly fine petrification whose mother is unknown to us. The same petrification had the shape almost of a Cunnus marinus (mollusc), yet did not seem to be a concha (bivalve). Other little shells were seen here and [looked] mostly as if gilded or coated with a tunica pyriticosa. Others were hollow, full of crystals.

(…) The whole place lay covered in wood for burning lime. True, the forests are insufficient, nothing whatever to boast about, only sparse and uneven.

Were these lime-workers able to have their way, the whole of Gotland would be cleared and flattened, as 20 armfuls of such wood are consumed for each burning lasting two days and nights. These lime-workers are no simple peasants, but a particular kind of foundry proprietor. The

The road continues along the bay to one of north Gotland's large industrial areas, Storugns. Here everything is white with lime dust, the trees, the road, the industrial buildings. Out of the crusher rattles a steady stream of rough lime chips, which are then transported by barge to various establishments in Europe.

I have the impression that Linnæus travelled through treeless country up to Fleringe and that the view from the church was open to the sea. That is no longer the case; the wood is dense all along the shoreline even though the pastures around the church are extensive and open. The stony fields lack vegetation; the odd gnarled pine has survived the winter among the grey stone, a withered butterfly orchid has also found nutrients among the stones. Around the church at Fleringe stand some low aged church stables, against the sides of which lean some beautifully decorated gravestones. "Jakob Pederson Hov 1682" it reads on one of them in uneven, lovingly sculpted lettering.

One of the houses which Carl noted and compared to settlements on Friesland was in all probability Grodda. The house, which is now a museum, was once an inn and so-called *spelmansgård* [musician's house]. It gives an impression of being almost cubic, shaped as a single dwelling of two storeys with few windows and a great deal of wall. A devastating forest fire struck the parish in the 1680s; the house was built shortly afterwards. To stand there on the well-worn kitchen floor looking at the large hearth, which still lacks dampers, is like being transported several hundred years back in time. A hole in the external wall is a hollowed-out sandstone with an outflow of the sink! The drawing room is light and friendly; small rooms for guests have been partitioned off with wooden walls.

Many guests would come here at that time, the main road north passing right outside. An innkeeper was obliged to provide guests with food, lodging and a change of horses. The musical era of the house began in the late 1700s. The men of Grodda were skilled at the violin and the vielle, and the wheel-vielle that they played can now be seen at the museum in Visby. "Waltz after Grodd-Jaken" rings in my ears.

In the twilight I cross the flat rock to the farmsteads of Hau. It is a risky road to take, the rock lies bare, moss grows on top of it, loosely packed limestone fills the holes. Had I been mounted, I too would have been afraid of losing arms and legs.

The crusher at Storugns quarry, Kappelhamnsviken bay.

Overleaf: Storugns at Kappelhamnsviken bay.

The Musician's House, Grodda, at
Fleringe, now a museum.
Below: Gravestone by Fleringe church in
memory of Jakob Pederson Hov 1682.

very terrain around the lime-kiln, with several works of spoilt limestone,
wood etc, even the buildings and the house of this minor foundry proprietor make these places resemble iron works, and such a limestone 'baron'
can sell 700 to 1,000 lasts of limestone per annum.

While here we saw across the other side of the bay something looking
like heavy smoke, but noticed that it was nothing but mist and haze
rising from the sea and it marched past us into the bay with the wind
and did not lift although the day was hot and it was 12 o'clock noon. It
finally thickened and flew up into the air like snow robbing us of the sight
of the sun, forming thin floating clouds. We were not a gunshot's distance away from the bay when we saw the sun clearly and the sea covered in
a dark blue mist or cloud, like the smoke from the mine at Falun, yes we
also saw the same rise from the sea on the east side of Gotland, lifting
after some hours and enveloping the entire bay in clouds. According to
the peasants' physics, this was winter cold which had remained in the
seawater. We deemed the great number of clouds to be a consequence of
this, and of rain, which the sea evaporates, resulting in the fertilisation
of the whole earth.

At two o'clock we departed from here, some allowed themselves to be
taken across the bay in small boats, and others rode around it, all of us
getting across in the same time, namely 20 minutes.

*

All the way from the shore near Fleringe church, three quarters of a mile,
the terrefacies (terrain) was similar with nothing but gravel ridges. The
church was situated in such a field, albeit smoother, quite steep and bare
on the sea side, a situation which, with the peasants' houses built of
stone, would soon have persuaded us that we were in Friesland, so similar was everything.

In the meadows around here there grew Moly (ramsons) and Porrum
oelandicum (sand leek) now in bloom so one saw clearly that it was the
same plant borkenbold, sed caule non revoluto (but the stalk was not bent
down).

From here our journey took us towards a village called Hau, a good
mile from Fleringe. The road was mostly over limestone flats where we
had to walk most of the way, afraid of losing arms and legs should the
horse stumble.

At the end of the winding road, the landscape opens to a densely leafy valley. This is where the Hau farmsteads lie, "the very best and most proper we had seen in all the land".

The farmsteads have a continuous history since prehistoric times. A large Bronze Age cairn by the crossroads, Norra gattet-Ar, and an Iron Age house in the nearby meadow testify to that continuity. Next to one of the farms there is the ruin of a medieval stone house. According to legend, a travelling farmer of the Viking era, Knobbur, lived at Hau. His harbour was Hau Grönu where his ship *Vindile* was moored when he was not away on one of his productive trading trips.

The farms are still among the most magnificent on the island. Nowadays, even the farm buildings are of stone. Maybe the south

Bare lies the rock between Fleringe and Hau farms.

Hop-poles at Hau farm.

Below: Stone floors and fireplace without a damper at Grodda farm.

Everywhere on these limestone fields there grew Globularia caule foliosa (globularia) which had finished flowering (…) Cepa sectilis (chives) also grew commonly here.

At about eight o'clock we arrived at the farm of Hau which was the very best and most proper we had seen in all the land, but it must be noted that there is no neighbour within three quarters of a mile, for on two sides it is cut off by the sea and a small mere, on two [by] sterile limestone flats. Two islanders lived near each other, each with his white-washed stone house, only the dwelling house was of timber, coated with tar.

Here one saw hop yards, gardens, especially with plums, and large leafy maple trees around the dwelling house which was partly walled in, and the rest enclosed and fortified with hewn wood.

Inside, the houses looked proper and tidy and the kitchens full of copper pots, 10 to 15 in each, larger or smaller. Nothing here looked decayed, everything clean and tidy, and there was nothing lacking; in the trees one saw several small cylinders of wood, hollow at the top so that starlings and other small birds could lay their eggs here and from the lush foliage of the trees delight the inhabitants with their constant music. A peasant who has eight cows and a horse, living far away in the forest, free from many a visitor, he is in the very best of health.

As in the southern parts of Scania, Småland, Öland and Gotland, the women wear their own respectable costumes and, without affecting new silly ideas, look fine when they go to church in the summer, dressed in their garments with the bodice sewn on to the skirt. The same bodice is usually decorated with flowery plush and hooked together at the bosom with silver loops. After the edict banning the peasant estate from wearing silk had been introduced, this their one and only fine good costume had to be left in the chest to be eaten by moths. Could not those in high authority allow these, who had never adopted foreign vanities for their adornment, to wear the costume which their ancestors had worn since time immemorial.

The houses at Hau stand solitarily in the open landscape. They are still among the most splendid on the island.

farm was the same as the one Carl visited? Hop yards and plum orchards no longer exist, but a dilapidated fruit orchard with old trees stretches towards the main road. The north farm was for some years a 'camp' school for children who would learn about the self-sufficient economy of the 19th century. It was later turned into a conference centre with a restaurant, lecture rooms and meeting rooms in the byre and stable. Anyone who is interested can do the heritage walk and visit a limekiln, a lime quarry and a tar stack which were once part of the farm.

28 JUNE (9 JULY) *The clouds gradually disappeared and prepared for us a hot day.*

We observed that the meadow in this spot was wholly red in the roughest places with the Cepta sectile (chives) now in bloom, alongside which there stood such an abundance of Antherico foliis gramineis (branched St Bernard's lily) that it covered several areas (…)

Down towards the marsh we found a plant Anthericum foliis ensiformibus filamentis glabris (Scottish asphodel), a plant never observed in Sweden apart from in Lapland, (…) but the Lapland one had smaller flowers (…)

From here we travelled to Rute church, about one and three quarter miles, on the way we saw nothing of curiosa interest. Rubia cynanchica (madder) grew everywhere with its flowers split into three…

We arrived at the church at 11 o'clock just as divine service was finished and the inquisition (hearing of the Catechism) was about to begin…

Entertained to dinner by pastori loci (the incumbent of the parish Matthias Kiöler), travelled towards Fårö island, leaving on the right hand side Bunge church (annexed to Rute) about a mile; from here there was half a fjärdingsväg to the sound. Immediately beyond Bunge church we saw meadows on the right hand side where there was nothing special except for Orchis muscam referens (common toadflax) and Athamanta (spignel). Here bushes grew of their own accord by the fences, like planted hedges, so that one could enter the meadow only with difficulty. They

Rute church.

9 July

It is likely that Carl and his party stayed overnight at Hau farm and then continued early Sunday morning to Rute church where a service was held. Now it is not possible to stay overnight at Hau, but I find my way to Fårösund and Bungenäs with its newly opened hotel in the old ramparts and batteries from the time of the Crimean War.

It is an unusual hotel, housed in the cement vaults in the ramparts, a little too damp and raw for comfort in the Gotland summer night, but the view across the sound from the public rooms makes up for much of the discomfort.

Rute church was built in the mid 1200s, the tower somewhat later. The medieval lime murals are by the "Passion Master". In the vaults are arabesques and intertwining patterns, probably painted when the church was newly built. In the bell chamber some grave slabs have been raised, one with a runic inscription. The party missed that one.

Then I must hurry to catch the ferry across the sound. I pass Bunge church, thinking I will have time to stop on the way back, just as Carl once did.

The ferry *Nina* takes me across to Fårö island and, unusually enough for July, I manage to get on the first ferry. The waiting time can otherwise be long.

The twilight is beautiful, the cows graze the shore pastures, some walking quite far out in the water which is obviously shallow.

The island is well grazed down, even the junipers have naked stems as far up as the sheep can reach. Well-built walls of stone wind along *were mainly ash, rowan, blackthorn, whitebeam, hawthorn. In that meadow there were more whitebeam growing in one and the same place than had been seen anywhere else.*

Bunge church was situated on a height, the eastern sea [Baltic] was visible where the ground sloped down to the sea, the land stretching further on the left hand side, but the forest was overgrown.

The sound between Gotland and Fårö was half a fjärdingsväg wide. (…)

After travelling three quarters of a mile from the sound we arrived at nine o'clock in the evening at Fårö church where we were kindly received by the honourable Reverend Mr Borg (Christian Borg). Everywhere the peasants were seen going around dressed in knitted jerseys, in white, blue and red colours, mostly very neatly and evenly decorated as though they had been woven, although they had been made only by the peasant woman's hand.

In this place, and particularly at Sandö island, which is a part of it despite being situated eight and three quarter miles away from here, half the parish hunt for seals here one year and the other half the next. The seal blubber is sold at 24 stivers per lispund and is dried in the oven. The fat is also used while it is still fresh instead of butter for frying pancakes. The seal pups are said to be a delicacy, and the people here were not infected with elepha etiaci (scab). (…)

There are eider duck on the islets, but they are not correctly handled in this land, because the birds are shot and, what is worse, their eggs are collected for making pancakes; but no wonder as long as Stockholm's southern fish markets are adorned all through spring with these shot birds; a good housekeeper ought to be content with (…) selling the precious down at a greater profit.

The Gotlander gets most of his money from lime, board, timber and tar, sold to Denmark and Germany, for the clear Gotland tar is then sold all over Germany, where it is used once a year for smearing the sheep to make their wool softer and better (…)

Chives.

the road, repaired with the assistance of the National Monuments Authority.

The church is different from other Gotland churches. Nevertheless, the heavily restored building has a medieval nave and chancel. In 1741 the church would probably have looked different: the east part would still have retained its original shape then, the tower would have been lower, and the spire not yet added.

I decide that tomorrow I shall try to track down what Linnæus mentions, such as important industries on Fårö, the forest with its timber, the quarrying and burning of lime and the production of tar.

The roads on Fårö island are lined with well-built stone walls.
Overleaf: The outbuildings at Langhammars farm.

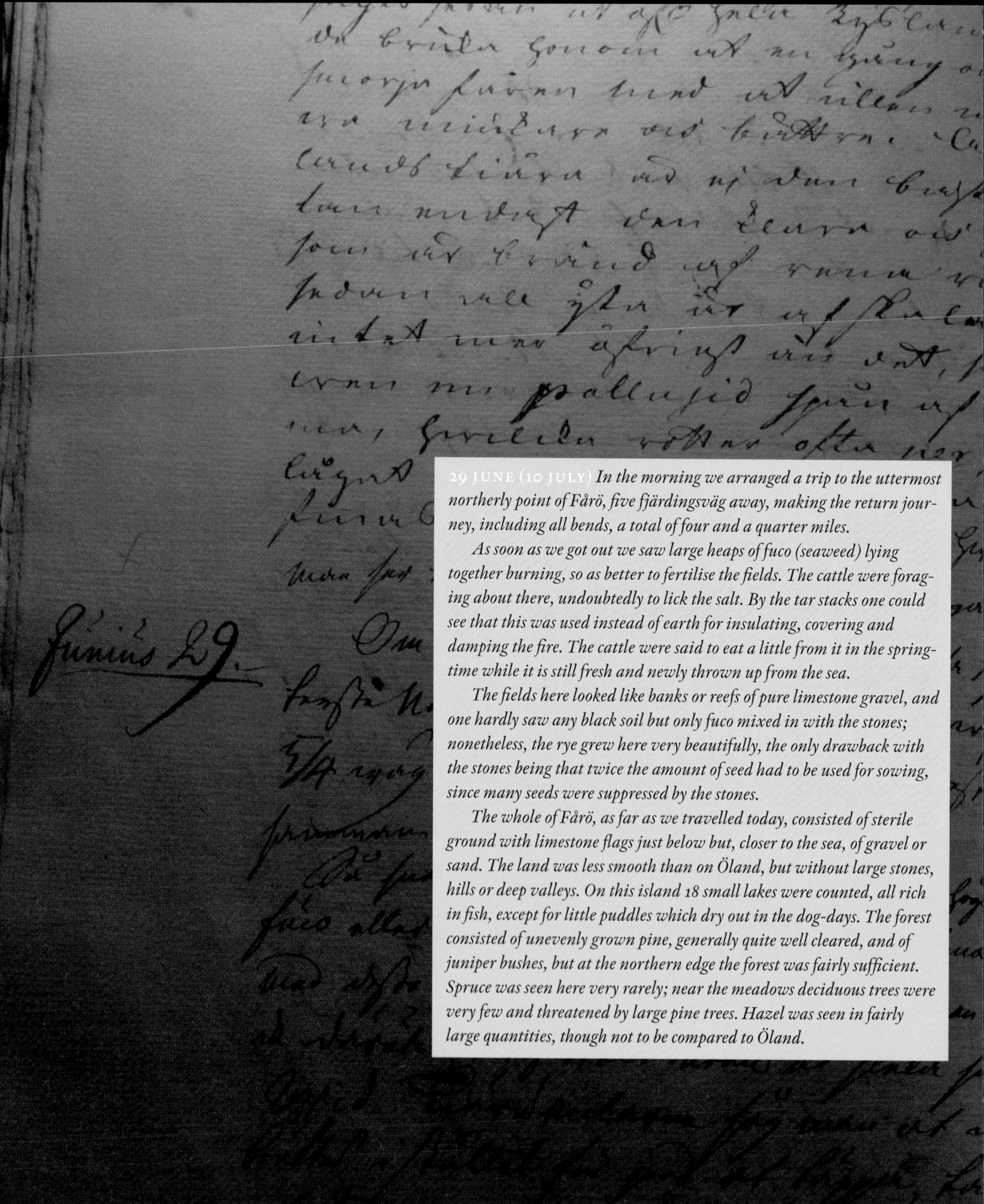

29 JUNE (10 JULY) *In the morning we arranged a trip to the uttermost northerly point of Fårö, five fjärdingsväg away, making the return journey, including all bends, a total of four and a quarter miles.*

As soon as we got out we saw large heaps of fuco (seaweed) lying together burning, so as better to fertilise the fields. The cattle were foraging about there, undoubtedly to lick the salt. By the tar stacks one could see that this was used instead of earth for insulating, covering and damping the fire. The cattle were said to eat a little from it in the springtime while it is still fresh and newly thrown up from the sea.

The fields here looked like banks or reefs of pure limestone gravel, and one hardly saw any black soil but only fuco mixed in with the stones; nonetheless, the rye grew here very beautifully, the only drawback with the stones being that twice the amount of seed had to be used for sowing, since many seeds were suppressed by the stones.

The whole of Fårö, as far as we travelled today, consisted of sterile ground with limestone flags just below but, closer to the sea, of gravel or sand. The land was less smooth than on Öland, but without large stones, hills or deep valleys. On this island 18 small lakes were counted, all rich in fish, except for little puddles which dry out in the dog-days. The forest consisted of unevenly grown pine, generally quite well cleared, and of juniper bushes, but at the northern edge the forest was fairly sufficient. Spruce was seen here very rarely; near the meadows deciduous trees were very few and threatened by large pine trees. Hazel was seen in fairly large quantities, though not to be compared to Öland.

The forest on Fårö is sparse in places with the occasional dead tree.

10 July

Fårö in July means, the population has doubled, busy traffic and many shops and eateries open for the summer along the major roads.

Linnæus does not state the exact route he travelled on the island. There are stopping places such as Ava House, the "northern point", and to the west where he saw reefs of sand a short distance from land, and Fårö church. His descriptions of the people, fishing, seal catching, tar production, lime burning, agriculture and marshlands imply that the party made detours from the main road. If you want to experience what Linnæus saw, you will have to venture on to the minor roads.

My trip north to Ava entails excursions to the marshes and taking small roads to the east. The roads here are winding dirt roads, a passing car is spotted a kilometre away from the lime dust, rising above the tops of the pine trees. The forest is a green stretch of low-growing pine trees, bending with the prevailing wind, emerging obliquely out of the sand. In places between the trunks there are glimmers of wetland, marshes with sedge. The sheep graze everywhere in the forests, and I pass several *lambgifts*, or sheep houses, with steep sedge roofs and limestone walls. At Limmor and Dämba marshes the fields open up, lined with deciduous trees. On the meadows at Klint by Limmor, the haymaking is long since over. The marshes are rich in bird life. Greylag geese, crane, corncrake, crake and marsh warbler breed here. Also scarlet rosefinch and nutcracker enjoy the place. In early summer marsh helleborine, loose-flowered orchid, early marsh orchid and common toadflax are found here.

A *lambgift*, lamb-house, on the road to Ryssnäs.

The inhabitants seldom sow anything but rye, for barley does not like growing on dry fields, thus the fields are also fallowed every two years. Rye produces white [sic] bread and as a rule enough grain for the farmer who, besides, is able to earn money from some considerable fishing of Baltic herring, cod, seal blubber, flounder, as well as from tar, timber and board.

Their houses are well built, the roofs only of boards, double, but the byres generally thatched with sedge as thickly as a double straw roof. By the farms is commonly seen some small stone house built of limestone, now with limestone mortar, now with bleke, clay and sand, although the bleke does not adhere as well as the limestone mortar. On the outside these houses are completely whitewashed with limewash and provided with tiled roofs, which adds no small ornament to the countryside. Yet, building in stone like this is not old but began in recent times. Fields and meadows are enclosed with fences, but the grazing is common over the whole island except for some small pastures.

After a trip of three fjärdingsväg we arrived at Ave farm on the eastern side where the people were in very good health. Building, arrangements and everything looked orderly. Here we cooled off in the burning heat under a large oak in the yard. Its trunk had a circumference of seven ells, the height of the tree was 17 ells, and the extension of its branches, or the diameter through the crown, was 44 ells.

This is where we saw the upright nets for catching seals which are set out around the stones on which the seals usually lie. (…)

Here and there along the shores there were large heaps of sand of white, fine, clear, even drift-sand driven up by the sea, but when we reached the northern point the whole area was filled with this sand, forming high uneven sand-hills. We thought ourselves in fact having come to the Dutch doins, everything being so similar. The unevenness of these dunes is caused by the Dutchmen's 'helm' or marram growing everywhere here. A strange grass which grows in the driest sand so prolifically in both height and depth that the longer it stays below the sand the more it branches out, namely from each joint. (…) This grass does the land doubly good, for where it grows the sand has to stay and will not spread further inland. The more the sand blows there, the lusher the grass becomes and the higher the hill; therefore behind these doins on the land-side one also sees lower sand-hills, the outer ones having removed from them

"Here and there along the shores there were large heaps of sand, white, fine, clear, even drift-sand driven up by the sea…"

Dämba is tranquil Ingmar Bergman country. The aged stone houses among gnarled apple trees have been meticulously restored without giving the impression of having had too much love lavished on them. They have simply been repaired in order to cope with yet another decade of tough autumn gales and icy winters.

By the cluster of houses at Verkegard, there is still an old threshing barn with its sedge roof extant although most of the other farm outbuildings have been provided with metal sheeting. Up in the pastures and the stony fields I find traces from the days of self-sufficiency; a small limekiln, several quarries and a tar stack. I ask Herbert Werkelin who is tending his currant bushes how long it is since they were in use. "Scarcely fifty years", I am told. "Is your house limewashed with lime from the kiln?" Yes, that is obviously so. Even the stone for all the Verkegard houses once came from the quarries. This is a cultural landscape which looks largely the same as at the time of Linnæus's visit. The small fields are the same, the sparse pine woods and the rugged heathlands are grazed in the same way as then, winding stone walls still frame the landscape. I pass by a little house at the end of a meadow. Greying wood, a single large, steeply slanted roof with gable walls of upright boards. "A prehistoric house", I think. House shapes die hard.

One of the oldest houses on Fårö is situated at Gåsmora; a stone house on two floors under a steep roof with few window openings. Linnæus and his party might very well have seen it. Today Gåsmora is very much alive with conference and tourist activities. New houses have been added, and the magnificent dwelling house looks strangely hemmed in and forlorn among all the new. Modernism dominates here with touches of Gotland tradition, clean plastered facades with large narrow windows in grey and with shiny metal roofs.

Along the road towards the sea and the sandy beaches at Sudersand and Ekeviken, the holiday houses, shops and eateries lie close together. The old holiday village at Sudersand with houses reminiscent of *lamb-gifts* tell of the simple holiday and camping life of 30–40 years ago. Now new winds are blowing; Gotland-adapted stone houses with one or two wings join minimalist architect-designed villas which in size probably surpass the owners' winter quarters. Road signs tempt with Indian fabrics, wood-stove baked pizzas, new potatoes, sheepskins

A limekiln, a tar stack and a small limestone quarry at Verkegards on east Fårö.

Seaweed and stones.
Lymegrass and murram thrive in the
sand dunes on Fårö.

all the supply of sand, and the growth of this grass is also poorer in them. The second practical use is that the land constantly becomes enlarged, while the sea daily heaves up sand on the shore and, unable to throw itself over the sand-hills due to their height, the sea stays outside, the grass creeps into the sand, binds it and makes the sand-hill wider and the land larger on the seaward side. (…)

In the doins themselves there were in places Formica-Leo (a kind of dragonfly), more colourful than before (…)

In the meadows where the odd field had been laid to pasture, the land stood quite yellow with Ranunculo erecto acri (meadow buttercup) and Loto vulgari (birdsfoot trefoil). Rocambole (sand leek) grew in all the meadows, which all over Gotland is called kejpe (…)

In Fårö church a painting was to be seen on the front gable, where 15 men were depicted who, in 1603, had walked out on to the ice to catch seals, when the ice loosened and carried them across to Sweden after which they had to survive for 14 days at sea on raw seal meat. Next to it are these stanzas in Danish telling the whole story. (…)

We had to remain over night at the Reverend Mr Borg's on Fårö, there being only one parish on the entire island.

Old greying wooden buildings at Verkegards, one only with slanting roof and gables. Right: The picture "Kutatavlan" in Fårö church.

and home baked products. I get off at "Kuten", a former garage where wrecked cars stand in lines, and which has become the trendiest place to visit on Fårö in the evenings, a genuinely nostalgic milieu where the old garage, with its pub lighting and rescued furniture, signs, ornaments, kitsch and props, is a goldmine for anybody with a yearning for the 1940s and '50s.

The oak at Ava was old already in Linnæus's day. Now it has acquired another couple of hundred years, reached a circumference of six metres and been properly restored with lime mortar, small stones and cement. The oak was given natural heritage status nearly a hundred years ago. Awe-inspiring, it spreads its wide crown across the yard, the furrows in the bark are deep and form a pretty pattern. I like to think that it stores inside it memories of the farm's history from half a millennium.

The Ava oak was old, Linnæus noted. It was awarded natural heritage status about a hundred years ago.

Fårö has preserved more old features of landscape and habitation than the rest of Gotland. One can get some idea here of what the landscape looked like before the great draining of the marshes. The island still retains its small scale with small fields and scattered habitation, surrounded by pasture and wood, often with a marsh or a part of the Baltic in sight. Due to its relative ruggedness, it has not been possible to cultivate Fårö in the same way as the rest of Gotland itself. This has meant that large economic resources were not available for extensive alterations to the building stock. It is only in recent years that building work has modernised.

I travel across sand dunes and through sparse pinewood, the ground covered in sprigs of cowberry. Then the field of vision opens up and the sea appears. It is a hot day but nobody is swimming at the Skär beach. I look out across Norsholmen, one of the sand reefs that Linnæus noted, and realise that all the bathers have chosen Nordersand for their swim.

The road to Lillhammars meanders between swampy areas, first Alnäsaträsk, then Norrsund and Bondansträsk. Earlier there was a sound here, dividing Fårö into two parts. The scenery is dominated by the sheep which keep the vegetation low. The wood is sparse with the occasional dead tree. The buildings at the farm of Bondans are positioned in an old-fashioned manner without the division into dwelling house and byre. The dwelling house of limestone is a small

so-called *parstuga* [two rooms and a kitchen], with a bake house; the byre shows a great deal of mortar facing and it has an enormous sedge roof; the cellar and the old outbuilding for the preparation of flax have stone roofs with grass. Rye of an old variety grows in the small walled shingle field. I wander around here for a while. My footsteps leave imprints in the thin scalp of dried grass. Then I come across another little limekiln, newly restored. Maybe it has already been used for burning lime? On a sign nearby I read that it is one of 72 limekilns on the island. Some were bigger and used for lime that was for sale, many were of just this size and used for the needs of the farm. 15 cubic metres of packing stone was burnt at a time here, requiring 35 cubic metres of wood.

Did Linnæus and his party see the farms of Langhammars? The south farm was in situ in 1725, as were the byre and the storehouse. Maybe it was one of the housing complexes that he noted, as "by the farms is commonly seen some small stone house built of limestone (…) On the outside these houses are completely whitewashed with lime wash and fitted with tiled roofs which adds no small ornament to the countryside. Yet, building in stone like this is not old …"

Below the houses, the sea and the Langhammarsvik bay open out with substantial seawalls. In the distance are the fields of shore bould-

Kuten's former garage, the trendiest place on Fårö, with memorabilia from the 1940s and '50s.

ers, *rauks* [a field of stones eroded into stacks], by Digerhuvud and the small fishing settlement Helgumannen with its wooden huts, old wooden boats pulled up on the shingle and a rack for fishing nets. This is where Baltic herring was caught over wrecks with lines put out directly from the boats, or cod was caught with a *pilka*, a short metal fishing rod with one or more hooks. One of the legendary fishing folk of the settlement was a woman, Båta-Bol, who had a hard life here and used to sail all the way to Visby with her catch. Others who have lived on in history are the seal hunters, depicted in the Kuta picture in Fårö church. They were rescued after having drifted for a fortnight on an ice-flow in the Baltic Sea in the winter of 1603.

I return to the ferry terminal late in the evening. There is no queue now, and the *Nina* takes me back across the sound.

Bondans farm on the way to Langhammars.
Left: Sedge roofing at Mölnors farm.

73

30 JUNE (11 JULY) (…) *Before leaving this place we had seen a kind of flounder called a butta (…) The small flounders varied, the eyes being at times on the left side, at times on the right side.*

Their [the Gotlanders'] language was difficult to understand, was spoken broadly, vocales usually became diphtongi. Nai, jau. Horse is russ or pert, saddle is fisflacku, a restive horse is fast, the cap-band is lausholk, mirror is söndagsau [Sunday-look], body-garment is baudordi, boy is sork, maid is pika, a little is en lille bisken.

We crossed Fårö sound in the strongest heat where we exchanged horses, watched peasants and their womenfolk dance. The rhythm consisted of uno pede longo altero duplici saltu brevi (long steps with the one foot, with the other short double hops, young schottische), the music was a bagpipe played by a peasant from Ösel island. That pipe consisted of an entire stomach of a seal, the modulator (the playing pipe) was inserted into pyloro (the orifice of the stomach), but the base was hanging down from the aesophago (gullet) and was blown into in fundo ventriculi (at the bottom of the stomach); thus no seam on the stomach. During this party Finnish lura [a beer] which had been brought by the people from Ösel was assiduously drunk, looked like white wax, was totally proscribed, prepared with red hot grey stones.

Here we saw the smoke-caves where flounder and Baltic herring was smoked, built underground with only the roof above ground level. They were completely air tight with no exit for the smoke, pitch black inside… The smoking is done with conis abietis et pini (spruce and pine cones) also with rotten oak and decomposed pine stumps and anything that did

Medieval entrance portal at Bunge church with a view towards the Bunge Open Air Museum.

11 July

Bunge and Lärbro churches are the biggest in north Gotland. The tower from the early 13th century may have had the same function as the citadels, that is, they protected parishioners in times of strife. Apart from that, the church is an entirely Gothic edifice. The murals are unusual for the island: large upstanding figures with a minor story showing scenes from their lives. There are architectural details and textile decorations aplenty here. An unusual matter, alien to the island, has been depicted: foreign armour with plumed helmets and magnificently caparisoned horses, interpreted as the martyrdom of the Theban legion. In the next scene the soldiers are naked, speared on thorn-bushes. The poor-box in the chancel, Romanesque in shape and sculpted in stone, bears the inscription "Lafrans made this stone".

The surrounding area is redolent of the Middle Ages; the high wall around the churchyard is of man's height to the west and provided with arrow slits. That such measures had been justified can be seen in the wooden door of the north portal which still bears marks from pike thrusts and crossbow bolts. Four medieval gateways lead into the churchyard. Immediately outside are the ruins of the medieval rectory, which was an unusually large and imposing building of several storeys.

Nearby is Bunge Museum, an open-air museum, which shows how the Gotland peasants lived in days gone by. The earliest buildings were brought here about a hundred years ago at the time of land reform. They were old buildings from the Biskops farm which were

Smoke-cave for fish, Bunge Museum,
and [bottom] as drawn by Linnæus.

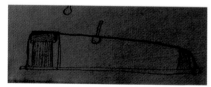

not give a flame, and continued for four or five hours so that the fish may not become too dry.

We travelled past Bunge church, which was annexed to Rute, and as far as architecture is concerned the most splendid we had hitherto seen on this island. Because there was talk here about a stone with an extraordinary property, Mr Adlerheim travelled east with a peasant to see it and found that, by relatione and specimine, it was a Spatum incarnatum lamellatum with a mica membranacea fissili alba (a reddish layered spar with a white schistous glimmer). From here we turned off the road to the left, travelled through the forest, which had mostly been cleared through lime burning, but in places there was a fair sufficiency of spruce which is otherwise not very common here (…)

Shortly thereafter we arrived at Malms where we saw eider down which was grey with white spots, hanging together, albeit loosely, so that it could be shaken without the down disappearing. This down the bird plucks off in the nest in order to cover the eggs and save them from cold when it has to go and seek food while brooding. The nest is usually found on the island of Furiln, which we saw through the window situated in the harbour, and it was usually under bushes, made up of much moss and many twigs, making cleaning [the down] difficult. For this a taut string of sail-twine was used with which the down was separated, as fine down remained clinging to the twine. The separating is done with a small wooden handle with a button, the string is twisted sideways, almost in the way milliners separate their wool, albeit scarcely a fathom long. Here a marker [ca 8ozs] of eider down was sold for ten specie karoliner, four marker made a small eiderdown which could be squeezed together to the size of a head, but very soon expanded again elastice.

Another almost similar down was seen here taken from a bird called jugås (shelduck) which was somewhat smaller than a goose (…)

Saw a bird here called grylle (black guillemot) which was smaller than a hen, pitch black all over except for the red webbed pedes (feet).

People told us that when getting betrothed, the peasants usually test their fiancées without anybody giving it a second thought. Consensus non ceremoniae faciunt matrimonium (mutual agreement, not ceremony, determines matrimony).

We arrived in the evening at Kyllej where we took lodgings with the mounted customs officer, strandridaren, after having travelled nine fjärdingsväg in the strongest heat, sweat pouring off our brows.

due for demolition. School teacher Th. Erlandsson got the local people interested, acquired land and re-erected the houses there. Today it is one of the largest open-air museums in the country with farmhouses from the 16th, through to the 19th centuries and everything to do with the self-sufficient economy: a tar stack, called *sojde*, a limekiln, a charcoal stack, fishermen's huts, a water sawmill, a fullery, a water grist-mill. Over a hundred buildings form part of the museum. Some are in their original locations, such as Strandridargården at Kyllaj, but most of them are behind the tall *standtun*, an old type of fence which enclosed the farms on the island already in prehistoric times.

I spend a long time wandering around the tarred houses which give off a nice smell in the hot sun.

Maybe Linnæus and his party took the road towards Nors and Alby where the forest is still extant and on to Valleviken bay. They passed Wernewik, present-day Värne, by the shore and saw Furillen at close quarters. The roadside was edged, then as now, with yellow chamomile and plenty of mullein. Then the scenery opens up. From the edge of the hill at Kyllaj we are met by a bewitching view of boulders, or *rauks*, lime ruins, harbours, sea and archipelago with the islands of Klasen, Fjaugen, Lögerholm and Furillen. Carl stayed overnight with the mounted customs inspector. I looked up some friends who spend their summers in an old lime baron's house nearby.

Mullein at Wernevik.

Outbuilding at Strandridargården at Kyllaj.
Overleaf: Flounder and pike caught in Bungeviken bay.
Outbuilding dating from the 17th century, built in *skiftesverk*, the old technique for building in wood, and with a sedge roof from Biskops farm at Bunge Museum.
View from the south point of Furillen towards the lighthouse on Lillgraut.

1 JULY (12 JULY) *Before five o'clock in the morning we were out at sea on our way to an island in the harbour called Furiln. This island was almost entirely grazed to the bare earth; there was nothing special here except for Scutellaria foliis hastatis intetegerris, Spergula, quae Alsine nodosa germanica, Prenanthes, Veronica spicata (Norfolk skullcap, spurrey, least lettuce and spiked speedwell).*

On the high hills, which were situated some short distance away from the shore, one saw how efficiently nature had arranged sheds and roofs, indeed houses, for the animals, in that the uppermost lamella of the hill extended six fathoms further out to the side than the lower ones. They were not only observed here, but nearly all hills [were like that] all that day, where the base or the part closest to the ground had earlier been more eroded by the water than the upper one, thus arranged like a house.

Pica marina (oyster-catcher) was called marspik here.

Eider duck is eaten here with great relish, but is first boiled or parboiled with hay, then fried or roasted when the train-oily taste disappears (…)

At 12 o'clock noon we returned from our sea trip. As soon as we had eaten we assumed our travel to Slite harbour.

We left Hellvi church (annexed to Lärbro) on our right.

Then we turned left off the road, travelling towards St Olof's church about one and a half fjärdingsväg from Kyllej. There we saw at the far end of the point a round islet and a whole semi-circle which had become attached to the mainland on two sides. On the seaward side of this islet

Morning by the shore.

12 July

During the entire 20th century, large parts of Furillen were closed to the public for military reasons and for the quarrying of stone. A German company had started the quarrying in 1904. More than a hundred people worked here in its heyday. Nowadays there is a fixed link to the main island. The lime industry has been discontinued, and large parts of the island are owned by Johan and Anna-Karin Hellström who have built a hotel, conference centre and restaurant in the old factory premises. Top class Scandinavian design dominates – minimalist, simple forms, and only well-known furniture and interior designers were used for the new and restored buildings and their interiors. I spend the night in one of the rooms with a view across the shingle beach in order, like Linnæus, to examine the island at five o'clock in the morning.

An oystercatcher keeps me company on the shore. Wild mignonette flourish with the odd clump of woad. My travel plan does not take in an excursion to the island of Klasen, and I am grateful to be able to note that the woad is still thriving along the stony shores, fertilised by seaweed.

The view from Suderudd towards the island's lighthouse is magical. The shore pastures are still lush and the grazing good. A time-honoured paradise with plants such as saltmarsh rush, red fescue, creeping bent, annual seablite, sea wormwood and seaside centaury. A lonely elder has taken root in the shingle, surrounded by tansy.

The hotel gets its energy supply from two wind turbines. Not far

View from Furillen.

Linnæus illustrated *rauks*, "the stone giants", at Kyllaj.

there was part of a church which had been about 20 ells wide and 40 ells long, about which a great deal was told, as was also of St Olof, and on a large stone, lying on top of the ground, was shown a hole the size of the top of a hat which was called St Olof's wash basin (…)

We were told how the men of Lübeck had formerly bought quicklime from here, by which the inhabitants became enriched (had an income) and the Crown received customs duty; but later that trade was proscribed (banned) when they began to jettison their ballast in the harbour and replace it with limestone; and they were forbidden to buy anything other than slaked lime, something, however, they later stopped doing and acquired the limestone from Denmark, limestone being necessary for covering bricks when burning them, thus getting the burnt limestone for nothing.

In the forest there was a large *Papilio diurnus, antennis clavatis, pedibus six* (an Apollo butterfly) (…)

We had two and a half miles from St Olof's chapel to Slite harbour. Today the forests were fairly good with more spruce than formerly which meant that there were more *Hypna* (mosses) in the forest; there was, however, no ancient forest here. In it grew *Linnaea Brunella flore magno* (large self-heal)

We ended our travels today with the same aspect as we had begun, for between Strandridargården and Kyllej and the limestone-kiln was, along with the sea bay, a downhill slope where many very large lime stones stood thick as walls, like ruins of tumbled down churches, between four and six fathoms high, generally narrowing towards the base. Those standing at the foot of the slope were taller, as all our heads were nearly in plano with the slope or field above. The water must therefore formerly have been that high and the land that much eroded, for there is no doubt that, unless these stones had been incorporated in a lime hill which had later been consumed by the sea, there is nothing else left but these ruins and these skeletons; for no limestone is generated above the soil.

Just before arriving at Slite there was, along the bay, southwest of the

from them I find one of Mr and Mrs Hellström's hermit cabins, designed by Mats Theselius. A simple little cabin in greying wood with everything you might need if you wish to get away from the stress of everyday life and find healing in a natural milieu: a stove, water, a comfortable bed, table, chair, paraffin lamp, a notebook, some books on the Gotland flora and fauna, warm socks and some apples. Linnæus would definitely have enjoyed it here!

I walk the east coast along meandering limestone-white wheel tracks to the *rauks* and the hollowed-out hillside caverns by the water which Linnæus saw as practical shelter for the grazing animals.

When I leave the island after a sustaining hotel breakfast which brought to life my taste buds as well as my aesthetic senses, the morning is still peaceful and, in the sound between Skenholmen and Furillen, greylag geese, shovellers and a few herons wade undisturbed by the cars on the banks. I pass the *rauk* field with its boulders and the fishing settlement at Lergrav, a popular stopping point for those looking for freshly smoked fish, so as to get to the southernmost point, called St Olof's Holm, via Hellvi.

The Norwegian King Olof Haraldsson came here in the early 11th century and, according to legend, christened the Gotlanders before continuing to Russia. The holm was called Akergarn at that time and,

A hermit hut on Furillen, designed by Mats Theselius.

Thyme on the shore.

85

Rauks on the shore. Furillen.
Right: Inside the hermit hut.

sea, a slope with similar stones of similar height. Bishop Wallin calls these gigantes saxios (stone giants) not unfittingly, for from a distance they represent statues, busts, horses and all manner of ghosts and devils.

Here I must not forget to mention an island where I went at half past nine o'clock with Mr Johan Moraeus and Fredrich Ziervogel, the other friends abandoning us for their own convenience. This island was fairly long, not particularly wide, entirely given over to pasture, and was called Clasen (…) The desirable dyeing grass Glastum (woad) grew all around the island, so lushly and abundantly that one had never seen it grow better in any garden. We wished that it had been sown all over the island instead of grass.

Also on this island towards its southern end grew a plant which had never before been observed in Sweden and it was a Scabiosa caule glabro foliis pinnatiphidis (small scabious).

The old factory buildings on Furillen.

to honour the event, a church was built here. It is still here, now rebuilt as a storehouse. The views across the heath-type landscape with its wide, terraced plateaus towards the sea are ravishing. To the west the area is characterised by the extensive quarrying of limestone. An old limekiln from the beginning of the 17th century when Gotland was Danish has been repaired; wild roses and elder trees have replaced fire and lime dust. As late as the 1950s, limestone was shipped from the harbour in the north. In the distance I see the silhouette of factories and smoke from Slite, Gotland's second largest densely built-up area, and still a centre of the island's limestone industry. It makes a strange contrast to the calm and deserted former work place on the scorched little island where not even trees and shrubs thrive.

I go towards Slite and from the viewpoint I look down into the grey-white 'underworld'. Small groups crowd at the Gunnebonät which conveniently has four square holes for our cameras. A different Gotland spreads out down below with ingenious transport links into an unknown landscape beneath us, the island underground.

The road back towards Kyllaj passes through white forests of low-growing pine and juniper, enveloped in lime dust. A desolate landscape of discontinued quarries and deserted limekilns, where the forest had once been fuel for the lime burning. A wind farm has been established here, the industry of the new era. The scenery opens up from the hill at Kyllaj with a wide view of rauks, lime ruins, harbours, sea and archipelago with the islands of Klasen, Fjaugen and Lörgeholm. Lörgeudd point has been a nature reserve since the mid 1970s. One of the preserved limekilns dates from the middle of the 17th century. Nearby is the old harbour. Maybe Linnæus and his party saw what I am seeing now, but then it would have been an area bustling with activity.

Strandridargården where they spent the night had been built by the mounted customs inspector, Johan Ahlbom, soldier in King Karl XII's army. He was also a partner in several of the limekilns. At his death in 1778, he owned most of the large farmsteads in the area, including Malms at Kyllaj, Pavalds at Lärbro, Valle at Rute and Strandridargården, which is a beautiful old house with interiors from the period. It is easy to imagine where Carl and his friends ate and slept. Unfortunately, the museum house is mostly closed, only open to visitors for a few hours at weekends in the summer.

Strandridargården at Kyllaj.

Overleaf: *Rauk* formations at Valleviken bay and view from the St Olofsholm church-storehouse, looking towards Slite.

2 JULY (13 JULY) *We had today intended to go out to a small island, visible from land, where Carlsved fort was situated, and also to another island, Asund, well-known for its rare plants, but now given over to grazing. Strong east winds denied us both; time denied us delaying, for the scythe had now had the audacity to violate our plants, and typhoid fever had already attacked two people in the house and 15 in the neighbouring house.*

We had hardly travelled half a fjärdingsväg before we had seen the sea on our left and a lake called Bogevik on our right, between which the land was quite flat, half a gunshot's range wide. In between, seven 'graves' had been deliberately dug out with a 'communication' one fathom deep and nearly a couple of fathoms wide, but the water in them was scarcely one and a half ells deep at this time with the bottom and water completely clear; at times the seawater rises into the lake, at times the fresh water runs into the sea, as at Norrström in Stockholm, all depending on the weather.

As the fresh water runs out, the fish in the sea are lured into the lake, whereupon the peasants are eager to catch the fish – done here very simply with hand-held nets only – which they can see with their own eyes and which they meet with their nets at both inlets. Across all of these the road was provided with bridges.

We left Boge church on our right hand, situated on the other side of the lake, and finally also the road itself. [Continuing] in the same direction, our tour led us to a sea bay where there was a headland, Thielward's bay

13 July

When Gotland became Swedish in the middle of the 17th century there were plans to make Slite – with its superb harbour to the east – a town and to move the administration there from Visby. Large fortifications were built, but the town plans came to nothing. Due to King Karl XII's wars in the early 18th century and the Russian occupation of the Swedish provinces in the Baltic area, the defence of the island became of immediate concern once again. The Karlsvärd fort on Enholmen island off Slite was built, and the fort would have been as good as completed when Linnæus visited the island. I am standing at Sjuströmmar, the outflow from the Bogevik bay, and see the fortified island reflected in the sea. It is an interesting island to visit for its defence history, but it is also an idyllic place for anyone wanting to study the flora at the edge of the archipelago. No trip out from the harbour for me, I am afraid; Linnæus had had to resist, and so shall I, concentrating instead on the seven graves and the fishing that Linnæus described. This is still a natural spawning place for many types of fish, such as ide or orfes, perch, whitefish, roach and eel. This current is not right for fishing with a net, but all along the long pier the pleasure boats lie in rows, and it must be wonderful to spend an early morning on the water going as far up as Boge church.

I think the Linnæus party travelled the narrow dirt road from Boge along the Tjäldervik bay to Tjälderholm island. The shore is close, the pastures rich in plants, and you can still sense the large marshes and the Vikeå river which were there before, despite the fact

Slite cement factory.
Below: A small pier at Linnæus's Thielward's holm, present-day Tjälderholm.

93

"The peasants here use ... for dyeing bright yellow ..." yellow chamomile.

The sedge roof of the byre at Vike Minnesgård enclosed with a tall wooden fence, *standtun*.

and Thielward's holm, said to have been named after a certain Thielwar who, according to a story in history, is supposed to have landed here and made Gotland his own before the time of the birth of Christ. This holm or islet was not big, somewhat elevated above the sunken land to which it had been attached; one could see that it had once been an island (...)

From here the tour went through the forest which was fairly considerable, particularly [stocked] with spruce, finally also Gothumå river, said to be the biggest in this land, although one could walk across it now in boots. Here, particularly on the right hand side, was a beautiful forest of tall trunks, the ground well cleared, no bushes, and all that most of the trees needed for [becoming] timber was time, and for a few trees to be cut down in order for the others to have a little more space.

After five fjärdingsväg we arrived at the church of Gothem or rather Gudhem. The rectory itself appears to have been a monastery, judging by the thick walls and vaults, and with a strange window in the vault itself, through which the sun could peer in at ten o'clock in the morning. On the outside it was little more than a good quarter of an ell, gradually widening inwards into the shape of an octagonal star.

The church was beautiful, a large runic stone lay in the chancel (...)

We viewed the meadows (...)

that the draining of the marshes in the 1890's transformed the bottom of the lake into cultivable land and turned the river into an excavated drainage canal. This is where Vike Minnesgård, a listed heritage building and museum from the days of the self-sufficient economy is situated, enclosed by tall palisades of the old type of fencing called *standtun* and hop yards. The byre is from the time Linnæus visited the place. It is a wooden building constructed in the old fashion, so-called *skiftesverk*, with a sedge roof, and built parallel to the dirt road. Inside the small courtyard the limestone dwelling house with a board roof is of somewhat later date. Attempts are being made here at traditional farming with pasture and grazing. The meadow, the hayfield close to the house, was flooded and fertilised by the Vikeå river and produced plenty of hay. The seaweed from the shore fertilised the shingle fields which yielded good harvests of rye and barley. Siblings Ole, Agnes and Emma still lived here in the 1950s in practically the same way as their forefathers had done in the 18th century.

Tjälderholm was probably an island once; now you can walk out to a picturesque beach with a small fishing shed and a pier. The surrounding area is rich in prehistoric remains: two old strongholds, a small burial ground, a ship's burial and Tjelvar's grave on the other side of the road. Legend has it that this was Tjelvar's home territory. According to the medieval tale, the *Gutasaga*, Tjelvar was the island's first inhabitant and is said to have been burnt at the stake and buried in a ship's burial.

The Gothemså river winds through the landscape, the fields are green and lush. I fail to see Linnæus's barley and rye cultivation. Now sweet corn is grown in fields by the kilometre. The water in the river is as low as when Linnæus was here. I do not try to wade across but assume it is possible. I search for the farm of Västerbjärs, Linnæus's Wästers, wondering whether I might come across the clay pit. Yes, on the way to Svalings on the right hand side by the river there are heaps of clay and carbonated lime, called *bleke*.

Gothem church from the 13th century, completed somewhat later by the stone master "Egypticus", is one of the biggest on the island and enclosed by a tall wall and trefoiled gateways. A contributing factor to the concentrated medieval environment is a stone fort, so-called *kastal*. The medieval rectory with its window has been replaced by the architecture of more recent times, but the medieval gateway to the house remains.

95

The clay pit at Linnæus's Wästers, present-day Västerbjärs.

Medieval house entrance by Godthem church.

Ryegrass, *Lolium sativum quod inter linum* is said to grow in many places among the barley, not in the rye; was said to turn people who drank beer made from it stupid and almost blind; it was also said that one would be preserved thereof if one smeared one's arm joints and fingers with the same drink. Here a great deal of ash and elm grew along the fences, all coppiced by saltpetre boilers who said they could not possibly do without this ash for cleansing away fat; it was also said that oak was not suitable for that purpose (…)

Yew trees grow, as large as spruce and oak, mostly beside marshes, plentifully in the parishes of Gothum and Boge. The down-turned, and as if overlapping, branches of the yew were used by the people for decorating their walls, the greenery being both colourful and soft. Could nicer wallpaper ever be produced? Would the guests survive if the strength that the old folks attributed to *Taxo* were true? (…)

Goats stay outside both winter and summer, getting no more [to eat] than what they steal for themselves.

We were told here that the famous clay, which in Stockholm was said to be got from the farm of *Wäster*, as well as from the *Gothumså* river, was situated half a *fjärdingsväg* away. The peasants showed it to us immediately, for it had been fetched from there earlier, and it was nothing but clay mixed with bleke, therefore useless for pipes due to its lime [content].

The peasants here use St Hans flowers for dyeing bright yellow, which were not *Hyperici*, but *Buphthalmi* (not St John's wort but yellow chamomile). The wool is first boiled in alum water in a cauldron, though not too strong an alum solution, dried, then the *flores sicci Buphthalmi* are boiled for quite a long time, finally the wool, and then dried.

Birch and alum produce a yellow, tending towards green; alum per se should not, however, be boiled *cum foliis*.

The wool turns green if it has first been dyed yellow in a decoction of saw-wort and sedum with indigo, for yellow and blue makes green.

It was pleasant and agreeable to hear in the church how the peasants and their wives sing alternate verses, one sex silent while the other sang.

We ordered horses from the parish constable as soon as we had eaten but only got them after the sun had set and that with much haggling, despite having straight away shown him our order from the Authorities, for the peasant here does as he wishes, holds neither parish constable nor county constable in any esteem, for he is not as accustomed to people as [they are] in Sweden; had to stay here over night.

Entrance portal to the church at Godthem.
Right: Road along the Tjälderviken bay.
Overleaf: *Rauks* at Bogeklint.

3 JULY (14 JULY) *Having rested overnight with the Reverend Mr Lutteman, we departed from there in the morning at five o'clock (…)*

A couple of large heaps of lifted stones were seen right by the road, thrown together long ago. Whether this had been done for the sake of clearing land, or [they] were tumuli sepulcrales (grave mounds), we do not know, the latter seems most likely.

On either side of the road there were extensive marshes overgrown with fen sedge.

(…) On the left hand side we left Anga church beside the road.

After travelling seven fjärdingsväg, we rested for an hour by Kräklingebo church, viewed the meadows; (…)

We had more than a quarter of a mile to Torsborg, a large, high and steep hill, flat on top, bare and rough. On its northern and western sides, abrupt and narrower, there were often large halls under the hill, yes, often as long as 26 ells, but the base underneath was wide, high and sloping. The top was rough, few trees, as fire had long since consumed everything. From here one could see many churches; all the forests were on the east and west sides of the slopes.

Origanum, Trichomanes, Sedum album et luteum, Globularia (marjoram, maidenhair spleenwort white and yellow stonecrop, globularia) grew here in such large quantities that if Sweden should ever order any, this is where to fetch them (…)

On the northeast side of this hill up on the very perpendicular steepness as well as by its base, there was Emerus Tornefortii (in fact Cornilla

Door lock at Anga church, beautiful medieval wrought iron work.

14 July

The region between Gothem and Kräklingbo is an area of ancient historic interest. Here you find plenty of coppiced trees by the houses, pleasant oak groves, overgrown apple orchards and remains of medieval houses and prehistoric burial places. Just before Anga church, close to the old dirt road, is a beautiful stone byre with its wooden anchor plates extant. I imagine the building to have been there when Linnæus and his party passed by and that it would have had a sedge roof then. Nearby is an old outbuilding for the preparation of flax with a stone roof covered with turf, meticulously restored with the aid of public funds. Close to the wild apple tree by the gable, there are visible remains of medieval stone house foundations and prehistoric graves. Maybe this is where he reflected on Tumuli sepulcrales.

Anga church is a modest little Romanesque church from the 13th century. Its interior is among the best preserved in Gotland and has decorative paintings from the end of the century by Master Halvard. An inscription on the wall tells how all the peasants of the parish had helped to build the church: "Made here this church, Högmund with four oxen and Liknvid with two oxen and Häggvid with two (...)"

The pulpit was painted in the year of Linnæus's visit. But the sedge marshes that Linnæus saw have been drained, and sweet corn is grown in the fields.

I stop at the meadow by Kräklingbo church. The hay has just been cut by machine, and the haycocks stacked in the modern manner. The trees look as if they have not been coppiced for some time. The sha-

The limewash paintings in Anga church are signed Halvard. An inscription on the wall tells the story of how the church was built, "Made here this church, Högmund with four oxen..."

St. Bernard's lily.
The previous two pages: Meadow by
Kräklingbo church.

Outbuilding for preparing flax and a
wild apple tree at Anga.

*Emerus, scorpion senna), a shrub, never seen in Sweden except in the
best orangeries. Had one hundred [people] told us that it grew wild in
Sweden we would not have believed it, unless fetched by our own hands
and collected at the risk of our lives. The frutex (the bush) itself was
nowhere to be found above the height of a couple of ells (…)*

On the side of the hill grew Hedera arborea (ivy) also in abundance.

*This Torsborg [hill] was measured in steps and found to be about
2,000 ells long and wide. It was enclosed with a wall of limestone where
the steepness did not prevent access, which was generally adequate per se
on the northern and eastern sides. If cost, men and labour were not spa-
red, nor gunpowder, it would be easy to construct an impregnable fort
here where there is no need for a roof; for there is water here which will
never dry out; nevertheless, the hillside ought to be blasted away on some
sides making it steeper, which would be easy because the hills split of their
own accord there. We seem to be looking at the high mountain Alexan-
der the Great had such difficulty conquering.*

View from Grogarnsberg hill.

dow is dense on the ground and the vegetation looks poor. "Natural heritage" reads the sign on an elderly oak which has been provided with supports. Maybe it was already here as a young oak at the time of Linnæus's visit.

In the early evening I reach Torsburgen. A few kilometres from Kräklingbo church is a small forest road, leading south past a row of three whitewashed old Gotland farms, the Hajdeby farms, then the desolate, burnt landscape takes over.

Linnæus saw a fort in a burnt down forest area. Today is no different. On 9 July 1992 a fierce fire raged on the southern part of Torsburgen, not far from Ardre Luke. The summer had been unusually hot and dry and the winds blew strongly from the south. The fire spread rapidly, burning down an area of nearly ten square kilometres. Despite the fact that the rescue services, the military and volunteers worked round the clock, it took them several days to halt the fire.

Overleaf: Burnt forest area at Torsburgen.

Life rises again from the burnt earth.

On the hill and also alongside it were trees hewn down, lying in the shape of a fence but ending up as a catisse (enclosure), which they used for capturing wild horses which they broke in and took.

At three o'clock in the afternoon we arrived at Östergarn where we were given a friendly reception by the Reverend Mr Lars Neogard who was one of the most remarkable of all Gotlanders. At his house we saw a descriptive account of Gotland, of its history, antiquities and language, completed long ago, compiled by the same clergyman, whom (with the exception of the great Polhem) we would with justification call *unicum forte gentis suae Phoenicem* (approximately: his people's one and only Phoenix). Alongside the church at Östergarn there was a high hill, cut off on all sides, like a son of Torsborg (…)

On this Östergarn hill the northeast side was a wonderful location, from its base one saw the church and the rectory, besides the wonderful cultivated fields and meadows, the green groves, the hills cut flat in the same way, and finally to the northeast and south sea bays, yes, and beside these on the far side, the blue sea gleamed all the way to St Olof's holm etc, so that no other place on this island seemed to us a more agreeable place for erecting a summer dwelling (…)

Here they were busy thatching a roof with sedge, which we were able to observe right from its inner structure. From the roof ridge to the eave were laid upright ribs, supported underneath by rafters. These ribs lay quite close to each other, less than a quarter apart, and had been hewn from thin pine, on which the outermost branches, or the ones that turn towards the sky, were left, to one quarter in length, on which the sedge could be hung.

Such a sedge roof can last for all of 20 years, provided it is not badly wrecked by small birds looking for worms there. It is strange that the year after the sedge has been cut, not the least green leaf pushes up from the root, but it stands with its pale withered stubble, before finally going green, and the longer it is left uncut, the lusher the leaves become. Thus, it can be cut only every five to seven years. Nor does it bear fruit where it has not been allowed to stand uncut for a long time, and therefore we also sought in vain its flower and fruit, which we had wanted to try to sow in Sweden.

Here at Östergarn the land was said to be at its widest and from here to Västergarn [the distance] was reckoned to be eight and three quarter miles; as from the northern point to the southern it was reckoned to be 26 and a quarter miles (…)

What meets our eyes now are solitary blackened trees and the beginnings of vegetation that thrives in burnt soil. A desolate landscape as far as the eye can see. But the scorpion senna bush that Linnæus saw here for the first time in the wild survived the fire and is still here today, as are hard shield-fern, Gotland anemone, and thyme broomrape. Kidney vetch, maidenhair spleenwort, stonecrop, madder, wild thyme, common rockrose, spleenwort, bladder campion, Alpine cinquefoil, creeping cinquefoil, blue fleabane, lady's bedstraw and northern bedstraw, mouse-ear hawkweed, wall-rue, large self-heal, small scabious, field scabious, globularia, spiked speedwell and the white St Bernard's lily were some that he noted when wandering around. I, too, saw most of them on my walk. On the marsh in the south there is cranberry which does not normally thrive on lime rich soil.

Linnæus would have been unaware of the fact that the fort is the largest prehistoric defence construction in the Nordic area. The steep natural cliffs, over 30 metres high in places, serve as protection for the fort. To the south where the terrain has less of an incline, a two kilometre long limestone wall has been erected, all of seven metres high in places. The wall which used to have several openings, one of them being Ardre Luke, was built in two phases, first during the Iron Age and later added to by the Vikings. The building material was limestone, quarried at the site, and a palisade of wooden poles on the top. Östergarnslandet was an exposed part of Gotland. The steep cliffs of the Grogarnberg hill would be the first glimpse of the island that an enemy would have seen when attacking from the east in those troubled times. But the place also had its advantages. Together with Herrgårdsklint hill and Östergarnsholme island, Torsburgen formed a watch system where the lighting of ward fires signalled that an enemy had been sighted at sea. As a defence it was almost impregnable. Large forces could be housed there, and there was plenty of fresh water, as Linnæus noted. The area is about twice the size of central Visby.

Gutasagan from the 14th century recounts that Gotland had once been so overpopulated that the Thing decided that some people would have to leave the island. Torsburgen was the temporary stopping place. Maybe they sailed to the islands of Ösel and Dagö and settled?

At sunset the ancient fort smells of herbs; this is where marjoram grows more abundantly than anywhere else on Gotland.

Seedpods of rosebay willowherb.

4 JULY (15 JULY) *At five o'clock we had to be out, despite the fact that we had only had little more than four hours sleep the previous night and scarcely five last night. Our tour was planned for the seaside to gather corals but on the way we were given for breakfast such a rarity as no botanicus had ever been given by a Swede, for here grew abundantly Sanguisorba major, capitulis sabrotundis, (great burnet), which we also found later today in equally plentiful supply and picked near Alskogs church (…)*

Melampyrum caule erecto, spica laxa laciniata (field cow-wheat) adorned the edges of the fields, and Christa galli (yellow rattle) coloured the field completely yellow at the base, more plentiful here than anywhere else.

On the shore itself there were heaps of corals, such as Madreporis cylindraceis, Cornutis, Entrochis, Poris, a lesser quantity of Madreporis multifloris (various petrificata) than at Capelshamn (…)

The windows of the farmhouses were not in the middle of the gables but close to one corner; the window in the wall or the side was hewn out as close to the corner as the other one on the gable. When we went inside we saw the reason, namely that both windows had to light up the oblong table standing close to one side, for the bed stood in the dark corner. The walls were of timber logs, sawn in such a way that one log could often provide three [boards], and these were not joined with the corners hewn into each other, but attached to each other in the same way as in a barn.

Hydrocotyle (marsh pennywort) flowered in the marshes (…) Behen album (bladder campion) was called tarald. Stalactites (stalactites) were

15 July

In Gotland's most easterly parishes there are still memories alive of troubled times from way back, worries of being surprised by enemy attacks from the sea. The old fort on the Grogarnsberg at Östergarn reminds us of the one at Torsburgen, a 30 metre high cliff, re-enforced with stone ramparts to the south. Herrgårdsklint at Gammelgarn also has a natural steep cliff to which limestone walls have been added on the south side. The parish church, too, has been provided with its own defence, a 12th century citadel constructed of large stone blocks like a massive metre-thick refuge against times of unrest.

I walk from Östergarn church towards Grogarnsberg hill and the sea. Field cow-wheat and yellow rattle still grow in the fields, painting the crop purple and yellow, and I discern Linnæus's observations about lesser twayblade, marsh pea, Yorkshire fog, skullcap, greater celandine, lesser celandine, longheaded poppy, sea plantain, marsh pennywort, fingered sedge and kidney vetch. The stony slope up the hill is bright with white limestone dust. In some stones I pick up I see the patterns of the corals and sea mats from the Silurian sea.

Up on the hill I face the same aspect as Linnæus did: the church, the fields and meadows on the one side and the blue sea, the bays and Östergarnholme with its lighthouses on the other. And I cannot but agree that this would be the best place for a summer dwelling.

But building restrictions are extremely stringent and, thanks to the shore protection and nature reserve, we are still able to enjoy the same view which pleased Linnæus so much.

111

In the region of När and Lau there are plenty of white limestone houses with tall chimneys.

Field cow-wheat.

Great burnet.
Right: Fleabane.

found here and there in the crevices in the hill.

Anthyllis flore rubro (kidney vetch with a red flower) grew on the flags, and *Pyrola multiflora nova* (wintergreen) grew in the dells (…)

From here our tour went to Alskog, leaving on our right Gammelgarn church (annexed to Östergarn). We viewed a number of sedge marshes, where we found a *Schoenus spica nigra, tetsile, compacta, mucrone prominente* (black bog-rush).

Reflecting on the trees that had been planted in the villages, we observed that a few deciduous trees against white chimneys (there being no shortage of lime here) are more decorative around a house than anything else (…)

The entire northern area of Gotland through which we had travelled consisted of limestone flags below the soil, but here at Alskog a different land begins, where there is mostly sand or clay and humus without any rocks. This region comprises Alskog, Garde, Lye, Stange, Hemse, Fardum, Leivide, Eistad and the parishes south of here, but not the parishes of Buttle, Eitelem, Loista, Linde, Garrum or Frojel. We immediately also noticed a difference in nature, for around the villages there were more deciduous forests of oak, hazel, hawthorn, blackthorn, ash, birch.

We stayed the night at Garde rectory after we had covered three and a half miles in hot temperatures. The Reverend Mr Lars Gardell was good-natured and had a beautiful face.

Gammelgarn church and citadel, so-called *kastal*.

Dwelling houses in bulwark technique with windows close to the corners, which Linnæus described, are preserved as museum houses in various locations around the island. Nowadays the farmsteads are dominated by 19th century limewashed stone buildings. But houses with white chimneys and tall deciduous trees are still embedded in the landscape.

I follow the small coastal roads with their shore pastures southwards; shingle, clay and seaweed make the shores difficult to use for today's beach loving bathing guests, and geese, waders, ducks, gulls and terns are left in peace here. Then suddenly, there it grows along the road, the great burnet, which, before coming here, Linnæus had only seen in "the very finest gardens".

The green really takes on a different character around the Alskog church. Sand and clay soils take over with deciduous trees, such as oak, ash and birch, and meadows with hazel, wild apple, and thickets of blackthorn and hawthorn. The open landscape unfurls with slightly undulating pastures and cultivated fields. I think Linnæus would have recognised this had he been here today.

The south portal at Gammelgarn with sculptures from the 14th century; here the banishment of Adam and Eve from Paradise.
Left: Shore meadows south of Ljugarn.

115

5 JULY (16 JULY) *In the morning at six o'clock we departed from here. Today the soil became far milder, greener, softer, blacker, richer in humus.*

We had set our minds on going to Lye church, which is an annexe to Alskog, but regarded it as unnecessary now after the Reverend Mr Neogard had informed us about the rare rune stone there which had been incorrectly taken down by Wormio, and reads as follows:

"Jacauper of Litlaronum (Lilla Rone). He had this stone made over his father Oluf and his brothers Lignved and Simon. May they and all Christian souls rest in peace."(…)

We left on our right the annexes at Etlem about three quarters of a mile from Garde whence there was a short three quarters of a mile to Närs church where we celebrated the Sunday.

At När we were received with undeniable courtesy by a very learned man, hidden here behind the bushes, namely Professor Nils Norby, who verily possessed professorial knowledge if ever anyone did. He entertained us all day with learned and solid discussions, for he was much travelled, had suffered more and read even more.

Towards evening we engaged a sensible Gotland peasant who was to teach us the botany of Gotland; he showed us Monorchin (musk orchid) and knew that this invisible plant had a very nice smell; he called Dianthum barbatum [=Deptford pink] Sarons blomster [=flower of Saron], Nemorosam (wood anemone) fageblom [=raking flower], Cynanchica (madder) madra, Scorzoneram (viper's grass or curled dock

16 July

Garde church did not provide Linnæus with "anything special to hand". Maybe he only made a note of the place before going to bed at the rectory. The church is one of Gotland's most remarkable ones and well worth a visit. It is one of the earliest stone churches on the island with many Romanesque features still extant. The surrounding wall is high with tall doors, gateways, in four directions. The entrance into the church is narrow. The windows which only exist on the south side are small and plain. Along the walls are stone pews set into the walls. The murals are reminders that influences came from the East – Russia and Byzantium provided inspiration. The baptismal font is also one of the earliest of its kind, created by the anonymous 12th century master Byzantios, and the triumphal crucifix is also suggestive of the 12th century. From the bell chamber in the tower, narrow winding steps lead to the roof beam construction in the attic, which is unique and richly decorated with a twist-patterned ridge-pole, a reminder of the 'design world' of the Vikings.

I travel past the Lau slopes and am amazed that Linnæus did not make a note of one of the most beautiful Gotland pastures, a part of the Brösarp slopes with sea and shore pastures within sight and lofty juniper and whitebeam along the hillocks. They mention passing "Etlem" (Etelhem) but must have been mistaken and noted down the wrong parish; he is instead more likely to have passed Lau, which fits in better with the road description he gives.

At När he stayed with the learned Professor Norrby who had been

Garde church with interesting Byzantine painting.

Four narrow entrance portals, one at each compass point, lead into the churchyard. This one even served as a parish storehouse once.

117

(Rumex crispus)) svinblomma [=swine flower], Millefolium (yarrow) pestilens blomma [=pest flower], Briza (quaking grass) bävergräs [=quake grass], Trifolium (red clover) honungsblomma [=honey flower], Melampyrum (field cow-wheat) kråkefot [=crow's foot], Myagrum (mitre cress) vill lin [=wild flax].

In the fields grew Sinapi sativum (white mustard) really plentifully; we were assured that the seeds were sweet and not bitter. Wild turnip Rapistrum grew in the fields; he showed us Napum sylvestrem (rape), a quite different plant which only grows in the fields by the seashore and said that before the stalk grows it is far better to eat than turnips, although somewhat thinner and was called åkerrova, field turnip; has not previously been observed wild in Sweden.

He told us that Cynanchica (madder) called madra, is much used here for dyeing wool red; the roots should be gathered before the cuckoo has begun to call, i. e. ante flores chentiam (before flowering), as they are then softer and give more colour, are boiled with the sourest small-beer to hand, usually made from mash which gives a stronger colour. Once all this has boiled, the wool is added while the decoction is still warm; thus stockings and such like are dyed bright red. The small-beer is called stan-debilla.

Pingviculam (common butterwort) he called fetnackor, [fat necks], and said that the peasant boils it in water, and with it rubs the boys' hair, which drives away lice and makes their hair grow better.

Now Christa galli, called penninggräs, [penny grass], by him, began to rattle their seeds as one walked among them, thereby reminding the peasant to cut his grass (…)

Having left the dry hilly region where mainly rye was sown, we now saw in the southerly softer soil more barley than rye, all the barley was Hordeum disticum which they called Gulland barley.

The party later whiled away the Sunday afternoon playing a pleasant ball game, called park, common here in Gotland and in Holland, requiring a measure of agility and speed.

We stayed here over night (at När) because our host and hostess had been the very best and most honourable, and we could not have found better.

Poppies are still seen in the Gotland cornfields.

educated in Germany, and was for a time the incumbent at Stettin, and spoke Latin, Greek, Hebrew, German, Talmudic and understood Arabic, Syrian and Persian. He also conversed with the local peasants and learnt the Gotland names for various plants; musk orchid was called *desmansblomma* [desman's, possibly Deschamp's flower], Deptford pink *Sarons blomster* [=flower of Saron], wood anemone *fageblom* [=raking flower], Hepatica *killingeblomster* [=kid flower], cowslip *gökblomma* [=cuckoo flower], quaking grass *bävergräs* [=quake grass], harebell *fingerhatt*, wild strawberries *rödbär* [=red berries], St John's wort *hirkumpirkum* [Hypericum], most of them well-known Gotland names even today.

Sunday was a day of rest but Linnæus still found time to inform himself about Gotland mustard and Gotland turnips and he found out about the island way of dyeing yarn, namely with the roots of the madder which were to be boiled with sour small-beer before the yarn was added. The sourer the small-beer, the deeper red the colour.

The party may have stayed quietly at the rectory. There are no notes of Linnæus having visited Närsholm, a flat peninsula some kilometres away. It is a desolate savannah-like grazing area with the occasional juniper and pine. Just before the road forks here at the southern point of the island which, in 1741, would probably still have been an island, the yellow milk-vetch grows with its yellow pea flowers, the only known habitat on Gotland. Sea-walls have been created by the waves and, along the Kroken bay, shingle bluffs dominate with three extensive spurs.

The bird life is rich on the shore pastures, ducks and waders, including both avocet, ruff and dunlin. I sit down next to an abandoned wooden boat and notice asparagus growing through its hull.

I decide to take the road via Lye church to see whether the rune stone Linnæus listed is still there: "Jacob of Litlaronum he had this stone made over his father Olof and his brothers Lignvid and Simon". The year was 1409. The farm Lillrone which was mentioned is still there, north of the church.

119

Wild asparagus growing out of an abandoned boat on the shore at Närshamn.

6 JULY (17 JULY) *We left here in the morning escorted by Mr Anders Broander, the professor's adjuncto and stepson. The ground looked very sterile with bare clay that was cracked, uneven and swampy in spring and autumn. What little grazing there was, however, was said to be very rich although Gramen sparteum norvegicum and Serpyllum (sheep's fescue and wild thyme) were nearly the only [species] to be seen here. By the meadows there were far more deciduous trees than before.*

On the overgrazed meadows everything had been eaten away except for Filipendula (dropwort) which shone with its white flower. In the forests pine trees grew, but no spruce.

In the meadows at Burs the musk-scented Monorchis (musk orchid) grew in abundance (…)

The flax was overgrown with fairy flax or Myagro (mitre cress).

We saw a whole field yellow all over with Rapistro (charlock); would have thought it had been sown over the entire field, had people not told us to the contrary. The barley was so suppressed by this wild mustard that it had not grown more than to the length of a quarter. We therefore persuaded the incumbent that he should simply make use of the seed of the wild mustard, collect it when ripe and before the barley ripens which would hardly please it; the idea being that the same could be achieved with this seed as from Kohlsad (rape seed) at Brabant, with which entire fields are sown for the sake of the oil. We also taught him how to extract oil from it, with which he promised to comply.

Might not the fairy flax also serve as oil in the same way for us as for foreigners (…)

17 July

The ground between När and Burs looks sterile even today with cracked clay. The slopes are dry, covered in wild thyme and clumps of flowering dropwort. Pine trees grow in the woods. Then I spot the thicket on the south side of the road. And it is indeed wild pear. Possibly 'great grandchildren' of the ones Linnæus noted more than 250 years ago.

He tried to encourage the peasants to extract oil from the seeds of purging flax, charlock and field turnip that grew wild, but without success.

The most significant discovery of the day was the sickle medick, hayseeds, which seemed to thrive everywhere, on the poorest soil in cool summers as well as cold winters. The grass could be harvested twice a year and needed no fertilising. The find was of such significance, Linnæus argued, that it alone would cover the cost of his entire Gotland expedition, and he hastened to write a report on it to the Academy, long before the travel report itself was presented.

The party took a detour up to Stånga church. Maybe this is where Linnæus saw for the first time the bench with the reversible back and which he depicted in his diary? Nowadays the bench can be seen in the regional museum in Visby. He must have sighted the church with one of Gotland's tallest towers from some distance. The portal into the church is one of the island's most remarkable monuments. In a wealth of sculpture and relief, the story of the childhood of Christ is told on the capital abacuses. In the tympana the coronation of the

Extraordinary sculptures at the south portal of Stånga church.

Wild pear still grows on the dry slopes between När and Burs.

St. John's wort.

The Reverend Mr Mathias Lutteman persuaded us to dine with him. We then viewed the very driest and poorest slopes on which nothing could grow; nevertheless, these sterile slopes had their own plants which are barely able to exist elsewhere; for example, Hernaria, Serpyllum, Acinos, Lagopus, Galium luteum, Quinquefolium argenteum (smooth rupturewort, wild thyme, basil thyme, hare's-foot clover, lady's bed-straw, hoary cinquefoil).

The incumbent escorted us by horse after dinner to his annexed parish, situated a scarce three quarter mile from here to the west. We looked at the church and the meadows. Gramen spica lavendulae (purple moor-grass) was an Aira with a small styl between the two flowers but not capitatus (provided with anthers) as on Melica (mountain melick).

The incumbent obliged us by letting us stay overnight where we were very well received. Just before sunset we wandered out into the meadow (…)

Between the fields there was an elevated, dry, steep slope and a wide field on which nothing grew except Phleum (timothy). In the far distance could be seen some green bushes (…) which were Medicago seu fenum Burgundicum (lucerne) which grows very beautifully despite the soil being good for nothing. It also grew very plentifully on the verges (…) Apart from this plant giving the best hay there is to be had, it needs no more care when being planted than simply for the seeds to be scraped down with an iron harrow; but we also learnt that whoever wishes to make use of it should not cut this hay until it has gone to seed, every three years, while during the other two years it can be harvested twice, for cut down annually before it has seeded, it will die out. Therefore it does not exist in places where it has been cut early (…)

Pyrus sylvestris (wild pear) grows quite spinosa (thorny) in the forests with rough fruit; Bellis minor (daisy) everywhere along the roads and from time to time Anagallis rubra (scarlet pimpernel).

Caprimulgus (nightjar) or night magpie screeched and rasped, as did the Crex (corncrake) in the far fields, and Melonthae minores or cock-chafers buzzed, rasped and spun around our ears and faces nearly flying into our eyes (…)

Chairs (like settees), as in the drawing, placed by the table with a backrest which could be turned to whichever side one pleased, were used here.

Virgin Mary is represented and the resurrection of Christ in the open-work gable above the portal. East of the portal there are unique built-in relief carvings which are unlikely to have been sculpted for this rural church. But it is the same master who created all the sculptures, the anonymous Egypticus. Maybe he was once here at Stånga and had commissions for other churches as well, which were never completed.

Towards evening I reach Burs rectory which is now a listed building because of its well-preserved surroundings with wings and aged outbuildings. In the main yard cockchafers attack me, and I find myself yet again amazed at the similarity between our experiences, regardless of whether one was travelling in the early 21st or the middle of the 18th century.

Burs rectory is a beautiful old milieu which has been heritage listed. Visible here are the byres.

7 JULY (18 JULY) *After the Reverend Mr Lutteman had shown us every courtesy we departed from here in the morning at seven o'clock for Rona, three quarters of a mile away. On the way we looked at a number of sedge marshes, examined its flower (…) We saw some ancient ancestral places along the way.*

At ten o'clock we arrived at Rona, the Reverend Mr Åkerman had not yet awakened properly, saying he had during the night been with a maniacum, for whom remedia pharmacephtica might have been more in place than theologica (…)

The people of Rona, who were known for having preserved their language and dress without aping new foreign manners, had nevertheless now become corrupted by foreign customs; one could not even see the peasants' baggy trousers, white knee-long vests, the black bodice garment ('commandment') laced together on top of the vest, let alone the shoes which were made to fit one foot only without need for shifting.

In the barley fields there was rye-grass (Lolium sativum), which makes people crazy and nearly blind when they drink the beer, prepared from barley mixed with rye-grass (…)

Under the hazel bushes and the ash trees grew Moly (ramsons) in abundance, which the peasants called rams, but Hypericum (St John's wort) was called hircumpirk (…) Cichorium (chicory) could provide all the apothecaries with enough chicory roots.

Hops were seen around the villages more today than before. Considerable meadows and leafy groves around Eke church, annexed to Rone,

18 July

Martagon lilies grow wild at the triple crossroads near Rone church.
Below: Bird sanctuary at Grötling-boudd headland.
Left: Drawing by Linnæus of a settee with a reversible backrest.

Between Burs and Rone, fen sedge is notably absent but at the three way cross roads close to Rone church, there is the largest clump of martagon lilies I have ever seen, with the possible exception of the one now found in the grove of Linnæus's house Hammarby.

The road between Burs and Eke and further on to Grötlingbo is still rich in ancient monuments. Next to Burs by the Häffind farms is the Bandlunde-viken bay, once a narrow sea inlet with remains of Viking habitation linked to the former harbour. In the 1970s a class of school children found a large Viking hoard here, Stavar's hoard, which is now on display in the Gotland room, *fornsal*, of the regional museum. Nowadays there is a 'camp' school in a nearby meadow where school children from Gotland can live like Vikings. Halfway to Eke is the next large area of prehistoric remains, Lejsturojr, with a number of large cairns and old foundations of houses, ancient fields and burial grounds. Close to the Uggarde farms is Gotland's highest Bronze Age cairn, Uggarderojr, 45 metres in diameter, and eight metres tall, a mighty edifice on the flat and desolate heath stretching to the sea.

A few kilometres south of Eke church is the privately owned, listed building of Petsarve, a genuine south Gotland house of sandstone with a flattish roof of sandstone flags, quarried at the headland of Grötlingbo. Further on within this privately owned property one finds the old barn and byre extant, also built of sandstone below steep roofs of fen sedge, the semi-grass which grows on the Gotland marshes and which Linnæus saw in bloom as he passed through this parish. The

Chicory.

The listed building Petsarve at Eke.

which we left on our right hand side three quarters of a mile from Rone.

The forests were passable, mostly pine; plenty of goats were seen, and fulbom (elder) in the gardens, otherwise called Sambucus. Most of the way the soil was sandy. In some places the grass more splendid than hitherto while others, being neglected, yielded nothing. In general the fields were fairly beautiful with rye, albeit sparse.

After a tour of a scant mile and a half from Rone, we arrived at Grötlingbo rectory at three o'clock. We viewed the church which was one of the finest in the land. In the choir we saw a rune stone inserted into the wall like a seat, (…) in the sanctuary lay another stone (…)

At four o'clock we went with the incumbent out to the headland of Grötlingbo. We saw the beautiful harbour, called Garnshamn, situated on the northern side of the headland. We tried to get out to some of the small holms in the sea, south of the headland, but in vain since the northeast wind was too strong.

This headland was totally bare, wonderfully green, on which several fine herds of sheep wandered, getting their feed here in both winter and summer without any roof for shelter; they are nevertheless the biggest sheep of all in the southern part of the land. The rams usually have two horns, rarely four, some have horns half split in two, of which the lower 'branch' was bent downwards, the upper one straight (…)

From this headland we counted a number of churches, particularly in the south, for where this parish ends the plain takes over which continues all the way to the outermost Hoburg hill (…)

The juniper bushes were said rarely to bear ripe fruit, usually no more often than every six or seven years, yet the green berries make as strong schnapps as though they had been ripe. In the meadows grew Malva erecta purpurea, folio rotundo, (common mallow) which had hitherto only been observed in Scania. On the ground grew Centaurium minus (seaside centaury), along the seashores Seriphium incanum, multifido folio (thale cress) in more than superfluity with a smell of lavender and a flower nearly opened (…)

Everywhere in the fields there were many tussocks, nobody could tell us the reason for this although we kept asking during our whole tour; we did observe, however, that they only existed in such areas which are water-logged in winter; and yet again there were no tussocks in areas within these that were somewhat deeper still, retaining the water in roof construction of the byre is most remarkable. It is held up by beams resting on the gables and vertical side poles, a form of construction that dates back to prehistoric building methods.

Linnæus observes the meadows with hazel and ash and flowering ramsons. The sand leek already had small bulb heads. He reckoned he had seen enough chicory to fill all Sweden's pharmacies (the root was used as medicine and was considered to have blood purifying properties, be good for constipation, hypochondria, and hepatitis). He also noted nettle-leaved bellflower and Yorkshire fog.

Rye-grass (Lolium verum), which the Gotlanders mixed in their beer to make guests crazy and dizzy, no longer grows in the barley fields, but elder bushes are seen in places.

The area is rich in juniper slopes now as it was then. Linnæus pointed out that, despite ripening only once every six or seven years, even the unripe berries made strong schnapps.

The Gotland sheep graze the meadows and shore pastures, but I see no rams with four or six horns, nor any of the goats, which had been so common in the 18th century.

I walk out to Grötlingbo headland to find out whether one can still see the Hoburg stack and all the churches in the south but, despite all the EU subsidies for the grazing of shore pastures, the countryside is more overgrown than in Linnæus's day. Just where the headland begins, a sign points to Angantyr's rojr, a cairn with a number of smaller cairns nearby.

In recent years the regional government has again taken up quarrying sandstone on the headland for roof flags. It is important that the building tradition survives, and that it will be possible also in the future for houses to have their flag roofs repaired. Foremost of them all is the medieval house Kattlunds, situated along the road leading south from the point. The property is a museum and can be visited in the summer.

The headland is rich in natural resources, the shore pastures and the nearby islands have an abundance of bird life. A number of different terns breed here, as do greylag geese, pintail, shoveller and teal. The furthermost point is now a nature reserve and visitors are banned between 15 March and 15 July. I sit down by the wooden fence that has been prepared for us bird watchers and watch the barnacle geese feed-

The museum house Kattlunds at Grötlingbo with buildings from the Middle Ages.

Flags were formerly quarried at Grötlingboudd headland to be used on the
roofs of houses. The quarry has re-
opened in order to make it possible for

the old roofs on south Gotland to be
maintained.

One of these rare roofs, seen on the way
out to the headland.

"Several small ancient ancestral places were seen in the neighbourhood." This is Angantyr rojr.

springtime until mid May. Where the headland began at Garnshamn was a large ancient sepulcral mound, with a circumference of 113 steps or ells, quite steep, heaped up of round stones as big as a man could barely lift. At a distance of one and a half fathoms from this mound there was a ring of large stones arranged all around it. We do not know whether it is Angantyr's mound or somebody else's. At four or five musket shots' distance from here to the north there was another somewhat smaller mound in the forest and, at one gunshot's distance to the north, there was the third and smallest one. Several small ancient ancestral places of interest were seen in the neighbourhood.

People are in the habit of boiling Sphagnum palustre molle (sphagnum moss) with beer to make fomentations (poultices) pro pedibus oedematosis, or swollen legs, and it has a remarkable effect. Nearly all the rectories had old stone houses for residences with very thick walls, built of solid stones inside and out, but in between filled with sand and gravel which pours out whenever a stone is removed from the wall.

We remained overnight with the Reverend Mr Nils Stenman after he had accompanied us for a whole mile and three quarters and today we had travelled four and a quarter miles in splendid weather.

ing peacefully at the water's edge. The black-headed gulls squawk above the water's edge. Is a raptor approaching? On a narrow path leading to Själgang on the southern point I stop in amazement and look at the tussocks in the pasture. Might it be, as Linnæus described it, that they are formed because water lies here all winter creating this bumpy landscape? The smell here is not to be mistaken, sea wormwood (Artemesia) spreads its fresh spicy aroma across the shore pastures.

Grötlingbo church with its low Romanesque tower and Gothic nave and chancel is, like most of the buildings at Storsudret, built of sandstone. A frieze in relief over round arches from the earlier 12th century church adorns the wall below the eaves. Hunting scenes share the space with heroes from ancient tales in no particular order. The beautiful carvings were quite simply already there on stones that were ready and suitable for reuse. The master carver was called Sigraf who also created the baptismal font in the church. I circle the church and note that it too lacks a window to the north. In former times evil was thought to come from the north and initially, churchyards had no graves on that side. Today, however, one of the greatest artists of the Nordic area, the Dane Asger Jorn, rests here in Grötlingbo churchyard.

The rectory where Linnæus and his party found rest with the incumbent Nils Stenman was from the Middle Ages. The building is still partially there, incorporated into the new one from the late 1700s. Today it is a private home.

"Everywhere in the fields there were many tussocks…" The tussocks are still fully visible on Grötlingboudd headland.

133

8 JULY (19 JULY) *From Grötlingbo our tour went to the outermost point of the land, passing Fide church on our left, annexed to Grötlingbo, after a journey of three fjärdingsväg. From there we had a scant half mile to Öja where we dined with the Reverend Mr Olof Helsing, who was fairly combustus (thick-set). From here he accompanied us to his annexe Hambra, which was situated on the eastern sea side three quarters of a mile, and then another three quarters of a mile to Wamlingbo where we lodged for the night with Dean Israel Johan Canutius.*

The meadows around Grötlingbo, Fide, Öja and Hambra were magnificent, more like groves and gardens than any ground, trees in superfluity, hazel, much birch, ash in considerable numbers, some oak. Where the hazel stood just close enough and there was enough around, the most splendid grass grew, from which one could conclude that the hazel does not burn the ground but rather contributes to it. There were also large open squares in these groves where the grass was poor as it did not get any shade from the hazel. The meadows stood covered with the following flowers: Parnassia, Filipendula, Linum catharticum, Alsine gramineo folio minor, Euphrasia, Lotus, Anthyllis Tormentilla, Brunella (grass of Parnassus, dropwort, mitre cress or fairy flax, lesser stitchwort, eyebright, birdsfoot trefoil, kidney vetch, tormentil, self-heal).

Here grew Monorchis (musk-orchid) with all its flowers on the one side; Helleborine purpurea latifolia (violet helleborine) had not opened its flowers. Branca ursi (hogweed) stood close together like hemp in the fields that had been turned to pasture. Here was also Tithymalus helioscopius

In the rectory meadow at Öja, harebells and orchids thrive, as do innumerable insects buzzing about at twilight among the dense thickets of hazel.

19 July

The view at Fidenäs is less impressive than in Linnæus's day. In the middle of the 18th century the landscape was open with views of the sea to the east and west and with an unhindered view all the way to the Hoburg in the south. Today undulating woods of deciduous trees and habitation extend to the east, while the views to the west of Burgsvik bay and to the north of the wind turbines at Näsudden are still discernable between birch groves and reeds. The deciduous wood here is what was formerly meadow and pasture, now overgrown.

The ancestral place, or *Ätteplats*, and the vaulted cellar at Vigan are signposted as heritage sites.

By the rectory meadow of Fide the air is heavy with the perfume of the flowering greater butterfly orchid. Traditional management methods prevail here: raking, locally called *fagning*, is done at the time the wood anemone, known as *fagning* flower, comes into flower, haymaking when the yellow rattle is in bloom, and coppicing, or *klappning*, to take care of fodder from the trees before the animals are let in to graze.

That is how meadows have been managed for 2,000 years. Its heyday was the 18th and 19th centuries; now, in the whole of Gotland only 300 hectares remain that are still cut with scythes, many here in the southern part. It does, nevertheless, represent 15% of Sweden's total area of meadow.

Today you can wander under the crowns of the oak trees and enjoy the birds singing in ash, hazel, wild apple, whitebeam, blackthorn,

Linnæus noted seaside centaury, thale cress, grass of Parnassus, dropwort, fairy flax, eyebright, birdsfoot trefoil, kidney vetch, tormentil, self-heal, musk orchid, violet helleborine, hogweed, sun spurge, corn buttercup, agrimony, chicory, mitre cress, knotgrass, purple moorgrass, rush, greater celandine, white horehound, St. John's wort and devils-bit scabious.

[Euphorbia helioscopia], Ranunculus echinatus, Agrimonia, Cichorium, Myagrum, Helxine convolvulus, Gramen paniculatum spicae lavendulae, Gramen bufonium, Campanula foliis urticae, Chelidonium, Marrubium, Hypericum caule ancipiti (sun spurge, corn buttercup, agrimony, chicory, mitre cress, knotgrass, purple moor-grass, toad-rush, nettle-leaved bellflower, greater celandine, white horehound, St John's wort) (…)

About a quarter of a mile from Grötlingbo we took a side road off the main road to the right where we viewed a round cellar, like an ancient ancestral place, where we saw a vault like that in a cellar, the interior constructed of hewn sandstone. On the floor was a quantity of earth, the exit on the north side, square holes hewn in the walls like cupboards. One armful of earth lay across the vault, full of stone and gravel, as though built with lime mortar. This was situated off the road in a forest meadow called Vigan. Whether this had been a fort for soldiers to drive away their enemies, or for priests to drive away vice, we do not know. The peasants recounted that a wide area around is called Wigan, about which they still to this day dispute the [placing of the] boundary marker stone, which formerly is not supposed to have belonged to any particular parish.

Where we took the road today we saw by the farmsteads, as well as in the countryside and by the churches, remnants of walls of large houses, of vaulted rooms, mostly with passages and narrow stairs into the wall itself, often three storeys high. Some said that these had formerly been fortifications, some residences for the first theologi, some residences for the gentlemen of the parish during the Danish time. Most of the walls had been ruined, however, which might still have been of use had the peasant provided for a roof.

A quarter of a mile from Grötlingbo on the right hand side was a dug out spring called Gullbacken. Not far from there were some quarries, and finally one saw on one's right hand the western sea pushing into the land its long Bursvik bay which, a bare quarter of a mile from its tip, was abruptly cut off by a sand bank, so that at low water one could cross over there, albeit very cautiously, for on the other side it was very steep and filled with mud. To the left was the eastern sea [Baltic] and to the southwest the outermost tip of the Hoburg hill. The entire ground was somewhat convex, but smooth without any tall stones and without any forest, with a sprinkling of small juniper bushes but closer to Fide all the juniper bushes disappeared, and the ground was smooth and green with small

NO·1694·DEN·16·DEC[E]MBER   FORDOM
YRCKIA·VARD·SALI·LAR.S·OCES·OCH·LIGER
ER·VNDER·BEGRAFWEN
NO·1688·DEN·18·MAY·DODE·   SALI·HV
TRV·DORTI·MATHIS·DOTTE OCES·OCH
ER·HER·VNDER·BEGRAFV
WA·DEM·BHDE·EN·FRYGDEF PPSTH

The gravestones at Öja church have been given a place of their own under shelter in the churchyard.

tussocks, only the meadows were rich in foliage. Towards Wamlingbo there was a little pine forest (…) In the churchyard at Öja we saw five rune stones and one inside the church but at Hambra there were seven in the church yard (…) We do not know how it has come about, but on most of the rune stones it is always and above all the name of the person about whom it is written that has been spoilt. In the same church yard lay a gravestone engraved with Latin letters and Swedish text, perfectly ready and prepared, which read that master Berren Klasson Coppersmith who died in 1691 was 305 years old, which must surely have been a good 305 untruths. Most of the day yesterday, although not everywhere, were seen simple stone walls of roundish stone, on top of which rested a couple of horizontal poles held in place by rods and withes, the staffs placed per parie on either side of the wall into the ground and thus themselves helping to keep the wall upright.

On the whole of the east side towards the sea we have all this warm summer mostly slept under down covers and usually under the light fluffy costly eiderdowns, where we have also noticed a difference.

In the evening at eight o'clock we arrived at the house of Dean Canutius of Wamlingbo, having covered three and a half miles in sunshine and strong winds from the northeast.

140

hawthorn and dogrose. Next to the road there is open meadow with red clover, bloody cranesbill and common rockrose as well as orchids, such as 'Virgin Mary's Keys' (Orchis maculata), early purple orchid, fragrant orchid, and military orchid; further in where the meadow grows shadier it is the greater butterfly orchid that dominates.

In the Öja rectory meadow south of the church, the hazel thickets are dense, the crowns of tall oak, ash and birch towering above. Herbparis, germander speedwell and maylily thrive in the shade; in the glades sea plantain, rock rose, yellow rattle, northern bedstraw and dropwort are scattered about. The orchids like it here too. Innumerable insects buzz around and there is a rustling of birds in the foliage – fly-catchers, warblers and tits.

Öja church was built in stages. The chancel with its apse dates from the early 13th century, the nave is somewhat later, and the tower was only erected in the mid 1300s. What we enter, though, is a large space full of atmosphere, with high vigorous vaults and sturdy pillars, the walls and the chancel adorned with 15th century murals and, in the triumphal arch, one of the most magnificent crucifixes of the history of art – the 13th century Öja crucifix. The mourning Virgin Mary on the left is a copy, however; the original is to be found in the regional museum in Visby and is probably the most outstanding of the medieval wooden sculptures there.

The rune stones which Linnæus inspected have been given protection and a place of their own in the churchyard. There are also other gravestones erected there with relief motifs and inscriptions.

On the other side of the road is the ruin of a medieval citadel, a so-called kastal, one of the many stone walls of houses which Linnæus saw on his way to the Hoburg. There are still a few of them to be seen. In addition to the museum house of Kattlunds, the citadels at Sundre, Kastle and Fredarve at Vamlingsbo are also open to visitors. Medieval gateposts stand by Unghanse farm north of the church, as also at some farms at Vamlingbo. Most of the ruins Linnæus saw were demolished at the time of the 'stone house resolution' in the mid 1700s when anyone who built a new house of stone was exempt from tax, and the dressed stone of the medieval houses could be reused. It is still possible to find medieval parts in houses of more recent dates or, when walking in the countryside, to come across a medieval cellar or remains of a wall.

South of the church at Hamra there is a faded midsummer pole; maybe "farm servants and maids ran all night long to their playgrounds", as Linnæus wrote on Midsummer's Day after having taken part in the celebrations at Visby.

Vamlingbo rectory with its museum dedicated to the artist Lars Jonsson, a Naturum presenting Gotland's flora and fauna in one of the wings and with gardens and a café. It is hoped that the garden will be restored to its earlier 19th century state with a rose garden, herb garden, kitchen garden, hop garden, orchard and maybe also a garden devoted to Linneaus.

9 JULIY (20 JULY) *Having rested overnight at Wamlingbo at the dean's, we went eastwards in the morning to the seashore to observe the outermost islet on the eastern side called Heligholmen [Holy island].*

Along the way we were joined by the dispenser at the Wisby apothecary's, Mr Samuel Adolph Lang, who left us at Slite.

The whole area near the small island was very sandy (…)

Plenty of Centaurium minus (seaside centaury) grew here. On the headland where we embarked there were no stone giants, but instead stone chambers, albeit without roofs.

Heligholmen was no further than three or four musket shots from land, was totally bald and rough, fairly level, from east to west 504 steps wide, from north to south 375 steps long. On the southern shore there were cliffs, two to three fathoms high, strangely excavated into several very singular chamber formations. As houses they only lacked roofs; only water sprites and naiads could live there, however, and none other when the southerly winds rage (…)

The velvet scoters' eggs lay on the ground; seagulls and Tringa (sandpipers and turnstones). On the inside of the island was a reef of sand [stretching] to land, yet too deep for riding on. Later we followed the shore for a while whence many different ducks took off.

The land became entirely bare and bald over about one mile. Some pine trees which were at first seen on the east coast were low, unable to grow tall, all with their crowns leaning landwards (…)

We were amazed that sheep could live on such poor grazing where

Medieval sandstone church, Vamlingbo.

20 July

Vamlingbo rectory now houses a museum in honour of the artist Lars Jonsson, a *Naturum*, giving an account of Gotland's flora and fauna, with gardens and a café. The dwelling house dates from 1779, the wings and steadings from a somewhat later date and therefore a different milieu from the one Linnæus visited. There had been a medieval rectory on the site; maybe that was where he stayed. Anyhow, the parish was the largest and the wealthiest in the Storsudre area and, for example, paid three times more than the neighbouring parish of Sundre when the Bishop of Linköping made his visitation to the island. There were fifteen medieval stone houses in the parish in the 1700s, and the rectory might well have been one of them.

The church is interesting, dating from the middle of the 13th century and built as a pilgrimage church, that is, intended for a considerably larger number of people than those living in the parish. With its three naves, nine vaults and rich murals, it makes a joyful impression. The medieval vaulted opening by the pulpit led to the ambo from which the priest once upon a time addressed the pilgrims.

The tower was made lower after being struck by lightning, resulting in a fire, in 1817. Maybe that was when the outbuildings of the rectory with their sedge roofs also burnt down? The tower must originally have been one of the very tallest in Gotland, visible from far away on land as well as out at sea.

I take the road down to the sea and the sandy beaches by the Holmhällar guesthouse. In the sand among the lymegrass the pro-

145

sea gravel covered the soil almost everywhere; yet they were fatter here than in any other place on the island. There was no black soil to be seen here, and the land lay like a ridged field in waves, all the way from the shore up to the uppermost and central parts of the land (…)

All of this had been tossed up by the sea, by the waves, usually once per annum, maybe, often none; thus the land increases annually through what is tossed up by the sea.

As we approached the outermost point there were some farms, fields and meadows to be seen. There grew Malva rubra (common mallow), Chicorium (chicory), Raphanistrum siliquis articulates (wild radish), Trifolium lupulinum procumbens (hop trefoil), none of which existed in Uppland. Opulus (guelder rose) was called qvalkebär here. One tree was standing perfectly firm, compact and alone, defying the powers of the weather: it was an apple-tree.

Nearer the point, the land was broken up to the east by steep cliffs, called Klivan. Out of the cracks in the hillside grew Rosa sylvestris (wild rose) with a white flower (…)

On the western edge of the outermost point towards the southeast, somewhat further out, was the most extraordinary thing nature had created on this land, namely a stronghold or fort, abrupt or perpendicular on all sides, except near the base where it caved in underneath with a concave side so that there was only one way of getting there. This was called Hoburg, known even to children through the legend of Hoburgs-gubben (the Old Man of Hoburg). We climbed this considerable height where the top measured 347 steps from north to south and 146 steps in width. This was quite bare, somewhat sloping towards the field so that should one wish to dig a reservoir in the rock, all the rainwater could be collected there (…)

Because there was no soil up here on the top it would be easy to carve out a cellar for oneself and dwelling-rooms and other conveniences. We wondered about one thing, to which Nature – never doing anything without a reason – had applied its utmost diligence, and had ordered here on the furthest point: why would Nature have left it so utterly infertile, indeed so that not even a beacon is installed here although so many ships have been wrecked on these shores, led astray by storm, dark and currents which always mislead seafarers, particularly as it is placed so high up, so far out, also particularly as seal oil and tar is produced here in this

Mallow grows along the verges.

Heligholmen island.
Below: Linnæus's sketch of Heligholmen.

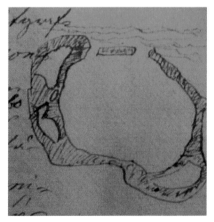

tected sea-holly and sea-kale grow. In the north towards Skalpvik a *rauk* field extends over nearly a kilometre: the "stone chambers, albeit roofless" which Linnæus noted. The *rauks* stand at the water's edge and up towards a slope, close together, sometimes tall like walls, sometimes low and rounded. The material is so-called 'marble reef lime', moulded from sealily stalks and stromatopora, forming beautiful greyish pink patterns.

Linnæus allowed himself to be rowed out to Heligholmen island, most likely from these fishermen's huts. I do what many adventurous bathing guests do at this time of year, I walk on the sand reef that Linnæus mentioned but which he thought too deep for riding on. At its deepest the water barely reaches up to my waist. It is a wonderful

Stony field with barley.

Sheep graze the shore pastures by the
lifesaving station Flisar at Sundre.

The Hoburg stack with the "Old Man" and [below] cave at Sundre.

land. *An English ship, laden with coal, was recently beached here, and nobody did anything about it. Or if a fort was ever erected here, might it not be the safest and most impregnable for the land in time of war (…)*

On the western side which sloped into the sea, marble rocks had been heaved up, with white and reddish granules, so large that 20 pairs of oxen would not be able to pull them. Whether they were from the Carlsö islands, visible from Hoburg in the far distance, or from some other place, is not known; what is known, however, is that they were not of the same species as the Hoburg [stone] (…) On the western side the walls were quite concave, in several places one saw large crypts as though dug into the base. On the northern side as well as the western edge of the land, there was something like a minor Hoburg with caves to the west, but further to the north there was another such one which on its western side had the largest cave inside it. We entered it. The room looked like a large vaulted cellar which eventually stretched far to the north, completely dark, where we did not venture for fear of falling debris, and it was called the Old Man of Hoburg's bedchamber. Our escort told us that a while ago some maidens had gone together to see the Hoburg and this cave, when some rascal had persuaded an old man to present himself naked inside the cave to let the girls see what they had been after.

North of Hoburg, about a fjärdingsväg, was a stone, albeit not placed there by human strength, on top of the earth, quite unfamiliar in this

walk in calm weather. The island is a bird sanctuary with no access between 15 March and 30 June. The velvet scoters are still sitting on their eggs when I walk across the island; gulls and terns hover above me giving me a not particularly warm welcome. There are *rauks* here too in the shape of chambers and caves at the water's edge, and the flat stony island is full of interesting fossils.

Linnæus rode along the shore towards the Hoburg. For me it turns into a long pleasant walk. At Barshageudd point there are extensive sea walls of rounded pebbles from the ice age. Linnæus counted 77 sea walls; today we know that they number at least 130. Sheep graze the area, newly cleared of brushwood, small pine and low-growing juniper – probably the same as Linnæus once saw. And I imagine myself seeing Linnæus a few farms away. Nowadays scarcely 30 people live in the parish all the year round.

The Hoburg cliff on the uttermost southwestern point had greatly impressed Linnæus and his party. Nature's own fortification, they thought, on the outermost point of the island, a natural place for a fort in times of war and for a lighthouse capable of guiding ships aright. Parts of the hill are now a military protection zone. The lighthouse did eventually get built on a height not far away. Today innumerable visitors wander on to the cliff to watch the sea in all directions, observe the profile of the "Old Man of Hoburg", one of the *rauk* formations, and visit one or several of the caves leading into the hillside. The island's most southerly restaurant is now situated here catering for hungry guests.

An old overgrown road leads from the lighthouse across the heath towards the "self-corroding stone" which Linnæus noted. It is called *Gullstajnen* [golden stone] and lies near the nature reserve on the Vaktbackar slopes. It is a large block of so-called Rapakivi granite brought here by the inland ice from the Åland Islands and which is crumbling away badly on the south side, turning into gravel of glimmering golden red.

Sundre church and citadel are the last stopping points for the day. Linnæus noted that there was a small deciduous forest nearby which ought to indicate that the rest of the parish lacked trees. He looked for rune stones as usual and found one in the chancel. Today a number of aged gravestones are placed in a garage close to Sundre old school

151

The protected sea-kale flourishes on the stony shores at Vamlingbo and Sundre.

The sandstone tower of Sundre church from the mid 1200s. On a mound nearby stands a citadel from the early Middle Ages.

Right: "The self-eating stone" at Vakt-backar, Sundre, a block of Rapakivi granite, brought by the inland ice from the Åland islands.

land, thus causing the inhabitants much thought. It was still three ells long, seven ells wide on the southern side, but on the eastern and western sides barely one fathom. The sun, which constantly bathed it on the southern side, had made it quite brittle and it was on that side only that it had eroded, its fallen gravel forming a kind of ancient memorial around it.

It consisted of a red spar, between the cubes of which shone a black mica which in places gleamed like gold where the sun had worked the hardest. Thus contained no metal.

Sundre church was situated in the far south of the land, three quarters of a mile from Hoburg and annexed to Wamlingbo. Its surrounding meadows had a small deciduous forest. In the church there was within the chancel step a rune stone, nicely engraved with foliage (...)

Beside the churchyard there was a citadel, quite cylindrical. The thickness of the wall was four ells, the height of the outside walls about seven fathoms, the diameter of the room inside was four fathoms, but the height, beautifully vaulted, was about six fathoms. There was no sign of a door here, but on the northern side there was something like a large window high up on the wall, the other openings were few and small, useless for pieces (cannons). A half-opening in the middle of the wall on the inner side gave the beginnings of a staircase, on which one could walk to the top of the vault between the double walls. From this we learnt that the ruins of the round towers which we had seen at Hambre, Öja and Fide had been such ones. People maintain that they are older than the churches, but strange that they and the churches are always conjoined. This citadel was now the most magnificent byre we had ever seen.

Not far away stood a splendid stone house of two storeys, excluding the attic, both vaulted and with thick walls. Now, because at the farms one sees mostly stone houses with such thick walls, it follows that all farmhouses of old had therefore been built of stone and not only for the gentlemen of the parish. It would be desirable for the peasants to be urged to do the same nowadays in this place which is treeless but rich in stone and limestone.

Close to Wamlingbo there was a small young pine forest.

The blistering midday heat was cooled by wispy clouds, through the openings of which shone the pale rays of the sun, about which people said that the sun was drinking water and tomorrow it would rain.

We returned at eight o'clock in the evening to Wamlingbo where we remained with the dean for a second night.

by the church, a small museum of medieval finds. The garage is interesting in itself: the medieval priestly dwelling house is likely to be concealed within its walls. The citadel which is well preserved, and which helped Linnæus and his party understand what the other round defensive towers in the Storsudre area had once looked like before becoming ruins, were regarded as "the most magnificent byre" they had ever seen. It still is. The grazing sheep find shelter here from storm and rain. Linnæus found a staircase between the outer and inner walls leading to an upper storey above the vault and enjoyed the enrapturing view of fields and shore pasture all the way to the sea. I do the same, but the "splendid stone house of two storeys excluding the attic, both vaulted and with thick walls" is no more. Neither are all the stone buildings, more or less ruinous, which he had observed at the farmsteads. Maybe it was a medieval step-gabled house at the farm of Vännes that he saw, or at Tomase? At the latter there is still the upper part of a medieval staircase in the pasture.

Left: The Hoburg stack at sunset.

10 JULY (21 JULY) *Before leaving here we viewed eight rune stones in the churchyard, although some of them were mere fragments, and we could find something legible on only three of them.*

Here we found a hedgehog (…) It was out feeding mostly at night, was principally found towards evening, usually wandering in pairs, said to build their nests out of hypnis (moss) (…)

From Wamlingbo we travelled northwest to the seashore where it makes an angle, forming the bay of Bursvik on the southern side. Here we viewed the old cave or the quarries where sandstone is extracted, from which the Royal Palace at Stockholm and other palaces are built. These 'mines' were considerable, numerous and extensive, though not deep (…)

One also saw large coffins, or linings for coffins, hewn out of the sandstone itself, also lids for them, ordered for Danish gentlemen, one of which could cost 100 daler silver (…)

The peasant's entire income and cash must be acquired here from the quarry, somewhat little from the sheep.

The sheep here do not go in flocks as in other places, but at the most four or five together, because if all of them went to one area their hunger would not be half satisfied on such poor soil.

We arrived at ten o'clock at the stonecutter's pier at Bursvik.

At 12 o'clock noon a couple of foreign skippers took us across to the isthmus, which was a promontory by the entrance to the bay on the northern side. The weather was pleasant, more than 20 seals peeped out

Relief carving from an earlier church, incorporated into the south side of Vamlingbo church.

21 July

Vamlingbo church is supposed to have been built as a pilgrimage church for considerably more people than lived in the parish. The interior is painted in grey and yellow, giving the trompe l'oeil effect of being built of square stones. A gigantic painting of the Archangel Michael is contemporary with the building of the church. This sandstone church is not the first one on the site however; it was preceded by a smaller stone church, probably built in the 12th century. Fragments from that in the form of reliefs are built into the south wall. The baptismal font by the anonymous master Byzantios also dates from the earlier church.

The turn off to Kvarne immediately north of Vamlingbo church leads down to the sea. Just before Grumpe fishing village I turn off north on to a small dirt road leading to Valar, Burgsvik bay and the quarries situated in a line along the sea.

The entire coastline has been chiselled by hard work. Shallow quarries show where the sandstone had been mined for the palaces of the time when Sweden was a Great Power and for the 19th century institutions and tenement blocks for modest wage earners. How many contracted quarry dust lung disease? There was no information about such matters.

The landscape is as poor and barren as when Linnæus and his students rode here; nutritionally poor, shallow marshlands, made up of *bleke* and lime-mud where reed and fen sedge thrive, and in between meagre treeless rock with dried out wetlands. The odd group of

The quarries lie in a row along the shore between Grumpe fishing village and Valar.

of the water (…)

The very best seal hunting ground on Gotland is by this isthmus, particularly on a sand reef which forms a semi-circle with an inlet at low tide, across which the seals tend to come for shelter; the inhabitants sneak in there then, setting up several parallel nets outside the opening, one outside the other, drive the seals out of the hollow and capture them in the nets (…)

Here were large cultivated fields, the crop so thin, the field probably not sufficiently fertilised, not drained, thus negligently maintained.

Along the shore by the crossing, where the water had been standing over the winter, there grew plenty of Salicornia (glasswort) or the proper potash from which soda is produced, the substance so vitally necessary for the glassworks and which is annually bought from Spain. Would it not be of much merit to enclose this, sow and cultivate it like any other cereal?

Here grew also Arenaria maritima flore purpurea, Potamogeton foliis natantibus, Onorpordon (sea sandwort, broad-leaved pondweed, cotton thistle) Crateagus or whitebeam was the only tree.

There was a Cimex corpore ovato, capite acuminato (hemiptera, sacred cross beetle) here (…)

Evening came upon us, a stinging storm began in the southwest; as sailing around would be three and a half miles, we set about tacking, the waves testing our courage and wetting our clothes. We arrived at the stonecutter's pier at nine o'clock.

Provincial Constable Jöns Winter of Botweda (1693-1770, Constable of the Crown at Hoburg District Court, resident of Bovide in the parish of Öja), who had accompanied us for two days and given us every assistance, lodged us in his house and in the village where we stayed overnight. He himself was the most attentive Crown servant we had met in this land.

All the nightingales, of which there were many here, had already fallen silent (…)

birch and sallow appear along the seaside as I get closer to Burgsvik. Growing on one of the many gravel heaps left from the quarrying is a whitebeam. How can it possibly grow without any soil?

Stone walls wind along the dirt road, dividing the land into different pastures, but there are no longer any animals grazing here. Maybe the ground is deemed too poor. It is a shame, as even these arid outlying areas need to be grazed so as not to turn to scrub.

I imagine that Linnæus travelled through an uncultivated landscape without any habitation. There may have been some wind shelters for the quarry workers. Now there is a string of second home plots, whitewashed little dreams for guests from the mainland who for a few summer weeks find peace by the sea, the rocky terrain, the varying vegetation on the shore pastures and the nesting migratory birds. Despite the habitation, a rare calm reigns here. The bird life is less intensive than in the height of summer, but there are still the young from the second brood in among the tussocks by the shore, and the terns dive-bomb towards my bare head disturbing the peace. There is no need to search for Linnæus's glasswort which he wanted to cultivate instead of buying salt from abroad. At the far end of the shore pasture nearest the water where frequent flooding provides the soil with a high salt content and where the shallow hollows with brackish water do not permit any plants other than extremely salt tolerant ones, such as glasswort and annual seablite to survive.

The air quivers in the heat on the lime-white road. The pools of water have definitively dried up, the area has entered its dry season. The smell of thyme and juniper is intense.

I pass the well-filled camping site at Burgsvik and reach the harbour and the pier which has replaced Linnæus's jetty. There is no boat to carry me across Burgsvik bay. I have to take the road through a flourishing summer community where the second homes lie side by side and the grills are switched on for the evening meals.

In the distance on the headland the wind turbines keep swishing around. They exist out at sea as well, maybe on the sand reef where Linnæus noted that the seals "peeped out of the water, one here another one there, on the way across".

A whitebeam growing out of the gravel by a quarry. How does it get its nutrients?

11 JULY (22 JULY) *The repair of our ruined clothes kept us indoors until seven o'clock in the evening, but we did inspect the meadows. There grew Seriphium (thale cress), Anthyllis flore luteo (kidney vetch), Scutellaria foliis integerrimis (spear-leaved skullcap), Ononis (restharrow), Anagallis rubro (scarlet pimpernel), Jacea nigra (brown or black knapweed).*

What we had hitherto regarded as Tordylium (wild carrot), and which we had described there as a small plant, was very large here, as tall as dill. The root was white, smelt of carrot, the stalk narrower.

Along the edges of the fields we found a plant which had never hitherto been observed in Sweden, Aster luteo magno flore (fleabane).

It is worth wondering here, where hazel grows in all the meadows and where fencing is so expensive, why people do not make themselves hedges out of hazel and hawthorn and thornbushes, all of which grow easily here, thereby doing away with the need for fencing.

They buy fencing and carry 12 fencing poles or trolor *over five miles, which make one* värpa *costing three stivers. 12 poles make one* börd *which costs one stiver, thus 24 stivers for the load, there being 24* bördor *in a load.*

The sheep which wander about outside all the year round without ever being under a roof are rounded up a couple of times a year, which is done in a manner similar to beating, the entire parish driving them together, as at St Bartholomew tide [the 24th of August] when the young are clipped, and at the time of Matthew Mass [the 21st of September]

22 juli

I too make the outing of the day in the evening out of curiosity to see whether I would experience the countryside in the same way as Linnæus did. His description of the landscape at Näsudden, likening it to a dough that had risen too much and with a hard desiccated brownish surface, still fits very well. This summer has been hot and dry too, the clay soil is cracked, the grazing is meagre, and the only plant that seems to thrive, now as then, is sheep's fescue. Sheep still graze the large areas down towards the sea where no trees bar the odd white-beam will thrive and where even the junipers are in decline. The landscape is magnificently open. Only the long monotonous lines of stone walls divide the headland and break the view towards the horizon.

On the outermost point, Boudd, and on the islands Flisen, Storgrunn and Lillgrunn, the bird life is rich; greylag geese and terns nest here and often linger in high summer during their moulting season when they lose, for a while, their ability to fly. A number of seals are here as well. At this time of year the water is usually so low that it is possible to walk out to the islands and actually see the seals with the naked eye as they lie on the stones by the sea. I wade out in the luke-warm water to the stony shore on the island which is now redolent with the smell of sea wormwood. But the memories from my early years in Gotland 25 years ago are reluctant to reappear. The landscape has changed unmistakably both since Linnæus's visit and since I came here for the first time. These days Näsudden is best known for its wind farms, and in recent years a jungle of wind turbines has grown

"The repair of our ruined clothes kept us indoors until seven o'clock in the evening…" Maybe it was in a room like this that he wrote his diary in the evenings?

A forest of wind turbines dominates
Näsudden headland these days, quite
unlike the landscape Linnæus once
visited.

up, concentrated at the outermost point and in the sea. There is much
wind there and the turbines rarely stand idle. I walk with the susurr-
ation of the blades in my ears and realise that a great deal of electri-
city is produced at Näsudden, even on a seemingly still July evening.

I reach Havdhem church just as the sun is setting. The uneven,
dressed stones and the absence of a water-table lend it a rather archaic
appearance. The chancel is the oldest part, dating from early 1100s,
nave and apse from barely a hundred years later. Inside the church, the
north window embrasure has fragments of Byzantine paintings as

163

South entrance, Havdhem church.

when the old ones are clipped, sorted out for slaughter and sale. The sheep are then immediately recognised by the marks in their ears.

We left our good provincial constable at seven o'clock in the evening. The road lay straight ahead, the land began to be covered in deciduous trees of birch, hazel and oak. On our left hand side not far away from us was the large bay of Burswik, on our right the churches of first Öja, then Fide and later Grötlingbo could be sighted.

After travelling about a mile we passed Näs church on our left. Immediately in front of that, the road led across a large field made up of nothing but clay mixed with bleke quite bare, cracked, bumpy, wobbly like dough that has risen too well. Here nothing grew other than Gramen sparteum norvegicum (sheep's fescue) and that so sparsely that there was usually a quarter between each stand (…)

We arrived at Habdum towards nine o'clock after a journey of two and a half miles, had intended to seek night lodgings with the incumbent of Habdum (Christer Wilspecht (1677–1745) but he was not at home then, having arranged a harvest home at his annexe Näs, preparing the hearts of his listeners for the Sunday with a schnapps and a glass of beer.

Therefore we continued to the next village to rest, but a virulent malign fever had in eight days taken the life of one peasant and now infected another, we stuck to our protective principle, mox cito tarde, cede, reside, redi (immediately, urgent, late, withdraw, stay, return); therefore having got horses at 11 o'clock at night, we had to ride on in the dark.

We left Alfwa and (Hemse) churches on our right and after one and three quarter miles arrived at 12 o'clock midnight at Fardum where we were given lodgings with the incumbent (Nicholaus Lange 1699–1765) although they grumbled a little because we arrived late in the night (…)

Havdhem rectory from the late 18th century is one of the most beautiful on Gotland.

found in the churches at Garde and Källunge. On the north wall of the nave I read an epitaph over the incumbent Christen Wilspecht, whom Linnæus never met, since he was then at Näs brewing small-beer. According to the bishop he was "stubborn and vexatious" and careless with the church accounts. He probably had reason to defame the clergyman who had in fact brought complaints about him to the King himself!

The rectory nearby is one of Gotland's finest, built in the late 1700s and now plastered in a warm shade of terra alba. The cockcha-fers – which Linnæus noted and which were caught and eaten by the rectory cat – still buzz in the tall trees around the rectory.

165

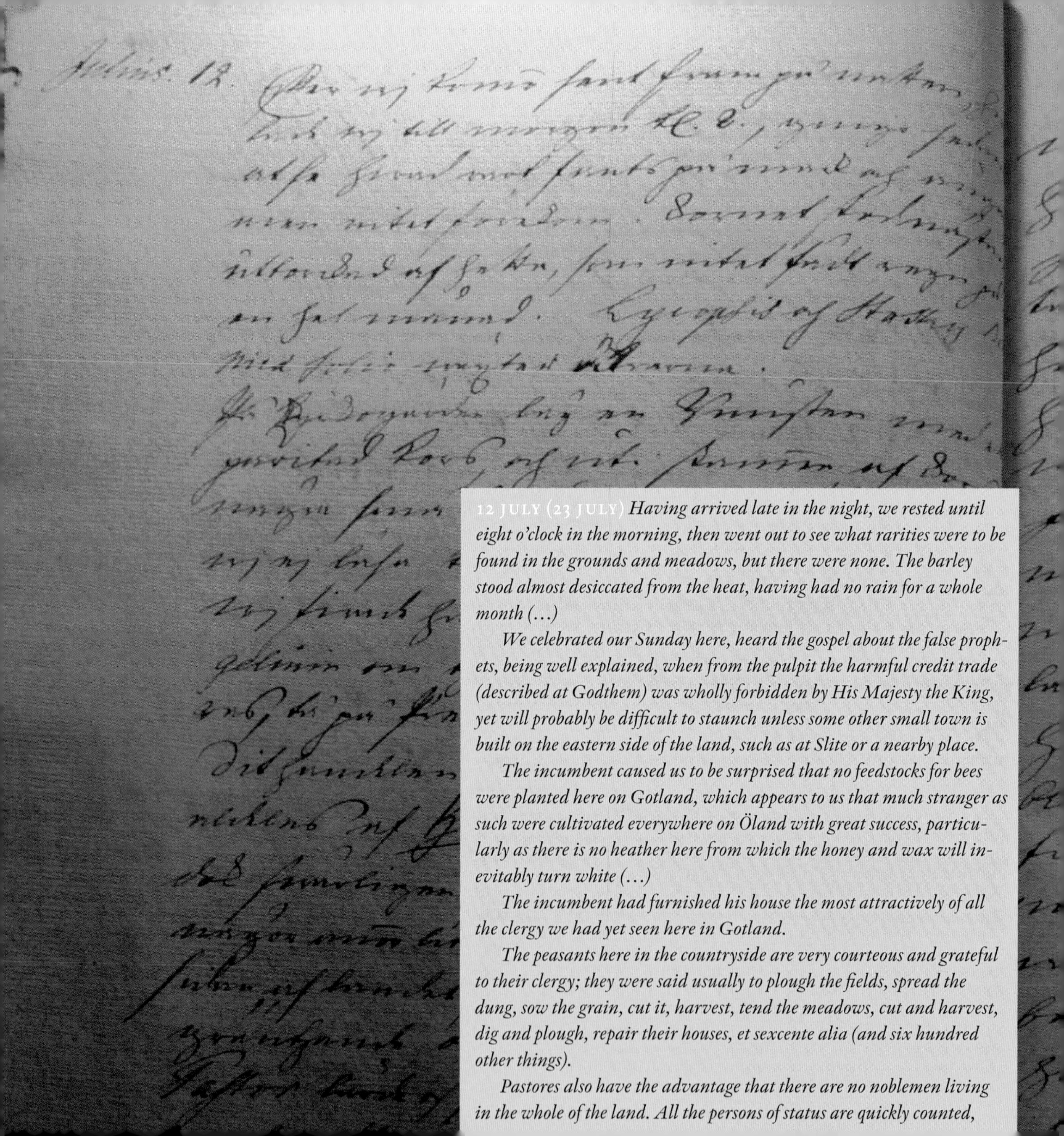

12 JULY (23 JULY) *Having arrived late in the night, we rested until eight o'clock in the morning, then went out to see what rarities were to be found in the grounds and meadows, but there were none. The barley stood almost desiccated from the heat, having had no rain for a whole month (…)*

We celebrated our Sunday here, heard the gospel about the false prophets, being well explained, when from the pulpit the harmful credit trade (described at Godthem) was wholly forbidden by His Majesty the King, yet will probably be difficult to staunch unless some other small town is built on the eastern side of the land, such as at Slite or a nearby place.

The incumbent caused us to be surprised that no feedstocks for bees were planted here on Gotland, which appears to us that much stranger as such were cultivated everywhere on Öland with great success, particularly as there is no heather here from which the honey and wax will inevitably turn white (…)

The incumbent had furnished his house the most attractively of all the clergy we had yet seen here in Gotland.

The peasants here in the countryside are very courteous and grateful to their clergy; they were said usually to plough the fields, spread the dung, sow the grain, cut it, harvest, tend the meadows, cut and harvest, dig and plough, repair their houses, et sexcente alia (and six hundred other things).

Pastores also have the advantage that there are no noblemen living in the whole of the land. All the persons of status are quickly counted,

23 July

According to the medieval tale, *Gutasagan*, the church at Fardhem was one of the very first to be built in the island. It was most likely a wooden church which, during the 12th century, came to be replaced by the present one of stone. It is a well-preserved Romanesque church, built of large irregular stone blocks. There are some ancient relief carvings in the chancel portal, showing the Virgin Mary meeting Elizabeth, both women with their hair plaited and dressed in simple Romanesque apparel, the way the women of Fardhem might have looked at the time when the church was built. There is also a man in a Viking helmet on horseback holding two large rings in his hands: are they fire rings and a solemn promise to adopt the Christian faith?

In the printed version of Linnæus's travel account there is a detailed section about the hop yard at the Fardhem rectory. Only male hop plants grew there which yielded no fruit. The incumbent had been advised to dig up the entire hop yard and establish it anew with the same plants, but that had not been a success; the male hop plants got the upper hand and suffocated any female plants.

Hops are still growing below the church and by the meadow nearby. They have found their way up the trees forming a luxuriant jungle along with the ground-covering ground-elder. Out of curiosity I examine plant after plant. They are all male hops, none of which will bear any fruit. A good 200 years after Linnæus's visit the incorrigible male hop is still flourishing here.

The rectory meadow nearby is lush. In early summer it presents a

Fardhem church.
Ancient relief at the south portal.

Male hops still thrive in the trees around the rectory.

only two district judges, one old captain in the entire land (excepting the fort and the town of Wisby), no more have we seen. Qui bene latuit, bene vixit; procul afore, procul a fulmine. (Whosoever lives unnoticed and happily, lives well, far away from thunder and lightning). The mail seldom reaches the countryside here all the year round, which is why they are not worried by newspapers but have to amuse themselves with what noise and changes that take place on the island and know little but what is caused by God and the weather.

Well entertained in the Stockholm manner, we went to the District Judge, Mr Laurin, who had invited us, sent his carriage for us, and lived a scant half mile away, where we stayed overnight (Johan Laurin 1693–1758, District Judge at the Southern Assizes of Gotland and residing at Boxarve, Levide from 1737) (…)

The cellars are generally useless in the summer here on Gotland, except in Wisby, exude acid into small-beer which is believed to be caused by the fact that they are built of limestone, which absorbs liquid, and become damp in certain weathers.

The houses here are all built with timber insertions [into wooden uprights]. The timber being inserted is cut into three or four boards, each three to four fingers wide. This makes the walls totally smooth, and [they are] often planed; in between the timbers tar is painted on the upper edge of the lower board, before moss is added, making them very tight. Apart from that, people use neither good double flooring, nor any filling [insulation] around their houses, because they who have no dampers [for the stoves] care little about the warmth.

dazzling splendour of orchids and meadow plants. Now I come across some clumps of marsh helleborine and broad-leaved helleborine. The ash that were previously coppiced very hard now tell the story of forgotten leafy canopies.

This is otherwise a fertile area which shows no sign of suffering from the summer drought. It is easy to spot that the fields are drained marshlands. In the setting sun the mist spreads over the former marsh domains. Rosebay willowherb and thistle thrive on the verges; birch avenues frame the kilometre long fields of rye, sugar beet and maize. Straight new roads lead to the fields. The area appears to me as empty and desolate as the cornfields in the American Midwest.

I return to the church and meet crowds of people. The whole parish and more have gathered as evening draws in. Football is on the agenda. Fardhem is clearly not devoid of people after all!

I continue in Carl's footsteps towards Levide which he calls Liwoistad. There he stayed with Johan Laurin, District Judge, residing at Boxsarve House. The countryside he travelled in must have been different on the edge of the large Mästermyr marsh.

Football evening at the sports ground, Fardhem.

Drained marshlands have become kilo-
metre-long fertile fields.

13 JULY (24 JULY) *Our host, District Judge Laurin, took the trouble to accompany us himself to the large Carlsö island which was his property. On the way we dined with the Reverend Mr Lyth at Ekstad where we saw over 60 peasant wives eat, sitting on the ground itself without tables, being treated to porridge and boiled Baltic herring, and we thought of how Christ had fed 5,000 men with two fishes and five loaves. These [women] were gathering hay for the incumbent, were his parishioners, and should therefore do it for free. In the churchyard there were two rune stones, one of which lay outside the church door, was two fathoms long and one fathom wide.*

After having travelled one and three quarter miles, we got to the shore where we embarked in two boats and after one and three quarter miles in contrary wind, we landed on the Carlsö island, which was a fortification in the sea itself, like Torsborg and Hoburg on the main island. Those two one does not want to call islands now, although in former times they peeped out of the sea which then covered the whole of Gotland: for in time the two Carlsö islands will, like 'Hoburgs', become part of Gotland. So steep, so tall, so hewn off on all sides, founded on stone – that is what the Carlsö island looked like, but was many times larger, more rugged, and had many more bights and bays. We landed on the west side in the middle of the island where some fishing sheds had been built and above which lay six stone cylinders, hollow in the middle, which had formerly been cabins or small redoubts.

As soon as we arrived on the island we were met by a large flock of

24 July

I travelled along the Eksta shore in the evening and saw the Karlsö islands like mirages in the far distance at sea. Today at nine o'clock the boat left Klintehamn for Stora Karlsö island. The day is still warm, a quiet summer's day. Filled with expectation, I see the magical plateau approaching. It is not the right time for seeing guillemots and razorbills on the cliff shelves. Most of the young have been encouraged by their parents to take the leap from their cliff nests, 20–40 metres above the sea, down into the waves. Most of them have managed the leap and are far away out at sea with their parents. But I am in luck. There are still a few families left on the shelves of the bird stack.

There are about 7,500 pairs of guillemots nesting on Stora Karlsö – the largest colony in the Baltic. The razorbills are fewer. The guillemots arrive in very early spring, lay the one egg at the beginning of May and by early July it is time for the fledglings to take the leap.

Nowadays one walks around the island with a guide. One can stay overnight and then have the opportunity to wander on one's own for a couple of hours before the boat arrives. But it is forbidden to walk around at random; paths are marked out and deviations are not tolerated.

The island rose out of the sea about 11,000 years ago. The precipices show proof of the sculpting power of the sea – the shore caves. Among the largest ones are Jungfruhålet and Stora Förvar, which have deep cultural layers left by the Stone Age people who stayed in

Wind turbine and timber storage by Klinte harbour.

Right: The Eksta coast is a nature reserve with shingle beach, wind-pruned trees and dead wood. In the background the Karlsö islands.

Wormwood spreads its perfume across the shore of Stora Karlsö island.

razorbills flying fast and swirling around the ship several times without fearing us. This bird is very rare and is called Alca hojeri, Anas arctica, is found at Rörstad in the Norwegian Finnmark, on an island in Ångermanland where it is called tormule and in a few other places here. It nests in cracks in the hill where it is steepest and impossible for people to reach it. It arrives here around the 1st of May and is said to leave its summer quarters at about Laurence Mass (the 10th of August). It lays only one egg, and it lies in the open.

It does not walk like other birds with its belly towards the ground, but upright like a human, displaying its white abdomen (…)

It exists very abundantly here. It is a strong swimmer and a good catcher of fish.

There is another bird here, very much like the other one, but somewhat smaller and is called grautle (black guillemot), it also walks upright, red below the tail, has red feet, the breast is black and not white as on the former, lays two eggs, nests on ledges in hills, but not above the height of two fathoms.

Another one (is a guillemot) is also to be found here, quite like the razorbill, but the back more grey-blue, the beak is narrow and straight, somewhat longer, has one egg, walks upright …

Towards the southern point of the island beside a large stone mound, like Angantyr's mound, but hollow in the middle, we upended a flat stone (because we searched in vain on both the Carlsö islands for a couple of rune stones, about which none of the local islanders were able to tell us) underneath there were, as had been said, a large number of juli (centipedes and millipedes) which we had never hitherto seen …

In the grass was a large heap of small molluscs. The cockchafers flew about in the late afternoon, the hedgehog ate them with great appetite, also grasshoppers and molluscs (…)

Night came upon us; we lay down in the fishermen's huts overnight.

Like a stronghold, the island rises out of
the sea. From the Eksta coast.

the cave, in the cliff east of Norderslätt. In the precipice below the lighthouse there are Korphålet and Rindhålet, hollows favoured by the guillemots for nesting. Grazing sheep and the need for firewood have kept forests away from Karlsö. The only tree Linnæus saw on his visit was an ash, which is still growing by the Bronze Age cairn Röjsu. But when the Karlsö Club was established at the end of the 19th century, a stop was put to grazing; the shooting of guillemots and razor-bills ceased; and replanting was begun on the island. Today Stora Karlsö is a nature reserve where walnut and red-cedar trees and St Lucie cherry bushes grow and spread all over the island.

Sheep's fescue still thrives in the shape of a ubiquitous low growing tufty grass. Carpets of stonecrop and wild thyme are spread out, and up on the meadow grow lesser meadow-rue, goldilocks aster and St Bernhard's lily. And there is still the heat afflicted plant which Carl and his friends found near the copse at Älmar – the 'Karlsö lettuce' with stalks as tall as a man. Shortly after three o'clock, it is time to return by the boat. Unfortunately, I had not booked in advance to stay overnight and all the rooms to let were full.

Large carpets of purple thyme greet the island visitor.

14 JULY (25 JULY) *Early in the morning we went out to the northern field where lay a large stone mound, one fathom tall, on top of which grew an ash, two fathoms tall and wide, was the only tree growing on top of the plateau and could be seen a long way out at sea. Around this one we saw a plant, which resembled Viscarium (sticky catchfly), affected by the drought, so that we were finally able also to see its flowers, as it grew everywhere in the dry and rough fields. It has been described, or one very similar to it, in Hortus Cliffortianus as never before having been observed in either Sweden, Germany, Holland or France, belongs to the genus Saponariae (soapwort) (…) This was also to be found on the small Carlsö island (…)*

In the dells there was much grass, standing in the way of one's feet, yet disdained by the sheep which were wandering up on the highest part of the rough plateau, particularly on the one side, from which the weather came, all according to its nature and the Creator's orders, something which ought to be observed by an economist.

The peasants said that they clipped the sheep only in the autumn at the Feast of St Bartholomew (the 24th of August) and at Matthew Mass (the 21st of September) but in the spring when the wool drops naturally they tend to strip the sheep, that is to say, pull off all their loose wool.

On the west side there was a room called Thief's Hole. One follows the lower edge of the high plateau through a narrow passage, a couple of fathoms down a ladder. Thereafter is a small flat stretch towards the steepest side of the hill, ending up so narrow that only one man can pass, having

The caves are many and deep on Lilla Karlsö island. Several bear traces of human habitation.

25 July

I have acquired a taste for islands. At ten o'clock the boat leaves Djup-vik fishing village for Lilla Karlsö island. I have brought a packed lunch as there is no place to eat there.

It is not possible to wander on one's own here either. On our arrival the guide is waiting and talks knowledgeably and instructively along the prepared route around the island.

Lilla Karlsö is higher than Stora Karlsö. A nearly circular plateau rises 66 metres out of the sea with precipitous cliffs and steep slopes. The island was below the sea during the most recent ice age; sea walls on the highest plateau formed circular patterns through the Baltic Ice Sea. Various antecedents of the present Baltic have left their traces in the shape of mighty caves, chiselled out at different levels in the mountain. The caves, Norder Vagnhus and Suder Vagnhus, are about 20 metres deep and show traces of human habitation.

Gotland sheep, a good hundred ewes and their lambs, along with the occasional ram, graze here nearly all the year round. Grazing is what characterises the island which is bleaker and more barren than Stora Karlsö. In a dry summer like this, the island gives the impression of being situated in the Mediterranean – parts are totally grazed down and a smell of thyme, wild marjoram and wormwood lingers over the scorched ground.

By Suderslätt in the lee of the precipice, elm, oak, whitebeam and ash grow. The young trees have been planted and are protected by enclosures.

the entire depth of the hillside on one's outermost side. Once one has passed this, there is a large cave in which some hundred men can be lodged (…)

In the field right beside the aforementioned ash, there was a plant which at first one took to be an Abrotanum campestre (field wormwood) exhausted by drought, but when compared to Abrotano (Artemesia rupestris, mugwort) which grew nearby, it proved to be a completely different and new plant in Sweden. The root was loose in the soil, not deep and firm like Abrotani, the stalk was shorter, thick towards the top, more upright, the entire plant hairier, the leaves as though shrivelled by drought, and the whole plant whiter and hairier.

It is said that all the churches and pillars, which were formerly built

Fishing huts and sea wormwood on Lilla Karlsö.

Guillemots, razorbills and black guillemots nest here too. They keep to the Österberg hill, and the guide does not take us there. But there are plenty of other sea birds too, great and lesser black-backed gulls, herring gull, black-headed gull, eider duck and velvet scoter. Some goosander pairs have built their nests in the trees, and house martins have 'cemented' their nests on the cliff shelves.

I eat my packed lunch on the shingle shore near the fishing huts, and an oystercatcher keeps me company. It looks as if it is accustomed to eating leftovers.

The boat takes me back to Klintehamn, and I am amazed at the enormous piles of logs in the harbour. Just as in Linnæus's day the farmers leave their cut timber here. Extensive sprinkling systems provide it with an even humidity while it awaits being cut up or sold to the mainland. In the vicinity the wind turbines keep twirling – the island's large source of energy.

I go to Sanda in the twilight. In the churchyard among the gravestones and 'greystones' [used by the Vikings for sharpening swords for export] I see a large flat stone dedicated to "Cofferdicaptain Petter Theofilius Bahr". Maybe he had traded in goods out of the Klinte harbour?

Linnæus noted that the church had splendid pillars. The present church was built around 1300 and was consecrated by Bishop Lars of Linköping. But there had already been an older stone church here. The pillars from that were used for the new building; they only needed lengthening. A beautiful baptismal font from the earlier church is still there, a work by the so-called Master Byzantios, dating from the 1100s.

I muse on the medieval house which Linnæus described as being situated next door. Could it have been the medieval rectory which has now become ruinous? Parts of the rectory have been incorporated into the present rectory of more recent date. Carl and his party did not, after all, stay the night with the incumbent of Sanda, but travelled on to District Judge Laurin's residence, Söderting, the present-day Ejmund House.

Trees and bushes are rare on Lilla Karlsö. In an effort to keep the island from becoming completely treeless, young plants are enclosed to protect them from the sheep that graze the island.

183

in Wisby and across the countryside, had come from a grey red-speckled marble from this island.

We left this high plateau or fort, perpendicular, hewn off on all sides, with so many caves in the sides, and at nine o'clock we went to the small Carlsö island, situated a short three quarter mile closer to land, which was equally steep on all sides and of pure stone with a bare plateau on top. Some trees grew on the plateau, such as hawthorn, whitebeam and ash. On the south side there was much greenery. Here grew Cochlearia, Melampyrum segetum, Pseudoliquiritsia, whitebeam, hawthorn, Tordylium (…) dauci species, Athamanta, Thalictrum floribus pendulis, Lithospermum verum, Isatis (Danish scurvygrass, cornfield cowwheat, wild liquorice, whitebeam, hawthorn, upright hedge-parsley, moon carrot, large meadow-rue, gromwell, woad).

Finally, among the many rare plants with which Flora has delighted us on this tour, she now offered us lettuce or wild Lactuca, which had not hitherto been observed in Sweden either.

After dinner District Judge Laurin took us to Klintehamn. Here was the greatest number of ships we had seen in any Gotland harbour, all of twelve of them, to take on lime, timber and boards etc (…)

From there we went to Sanda. Not far from the church were the walls of an old square house or tower, the bottom storey of which consisted of two vaults, the upper one with a beautiful pillar in the centre. All the window slits on the ground floor narrow. The inhabitants believed these houses to have been built at the time when piracy flourished in the Baltic, in order hurriedly to find shelter for themselves and their property within these walls. On top of the vault grew Epilobium maximum (willowherb).

The church was built of dressed marble with splendid pillars inside.

The lively District Judge, Mr Laurin, took us to his residence which was on our way and is called Söderting, where we remained overnight.

Relief on the 12th century baptismal font in Sanda church.

After stuffing a couple of birds we went towards Roma monastery, two and a half miles on a dusty road.

In Mästerby churchyard a rune stone was read (…)

Ossea (dogwood) grew in a shrubbery more abundantly than we had hitherto seen, and three fathoms tall, which had newly opened its white flower racemes. Buphthalmum (yellow chamomile) turned the fallow fields yellow, Aster salicis folio (fleabane) now began to come into flower in low-lying meadows, the sides of the cultivated fields now made a fine show of blue Cichorium (chicory) (…)

We arrived at the monastery where Provincial Governor Hökerstedt resided, a place which is very well situated and well built with the most splendid stone houses of all the governors' residences, beautiful gardens, delightful meadows to the south, wide cultivated fields, both enclosed by compact ever-green forests, which encompassed this splendour as though with walls. To the north the church was seen in linea recta (in direct line) towards the road. Here we saw a terrible metamorphosis, which was never described by Ovid, namely a splendid monastery transformed into a byre. Now oxen and cows low where once monks and nuns chanted, now dung and excrement stink where once aromatic incense spread its perfume. Thus, time can confound everything, yet one thing is certain that this room is the most magnificent byre that has ever existed in Sweden, built of marble, dressed and polished.

We remained overnight at Kongsgården (King's House), were received and entertained with every kindness and favour by Governor Hökerstedt's wife.

"Fleabane now began to come into flower in low-lying meadows…"

26 July

In the early morning I travel in the direction of Sanda church. The verges are edged with chicory, poppy, wild carrot, thistle, rest-harrow, viper's bugloss and lady's bedstraw. Vegetation is lush here despite the summer drought. The meadows are newly cut, and the harvest parcelled up into large white eggs, "cattle eggs", the farmer calls them. Mustard is grown in the fields.

Once upon a time elm was planted along the road and regularly trimmed. The tree crowns were kept low and the trunks cleared of any shoots. Nobody manages the avenue any more. Now it is the large machines of the roads department that chop off the branches on the road side with the result that the avenue of trees has turned into a tall, dense, impenetrable hedge. Above the hedge one can see the sprawl of lacerated tree crowns.

"Pick Your Own Strawberries" a sign reads, and a couple of other ones "Saddlery" and "Guest House for Dogs". Near the rectory where Linnæus and his party stayed overnight, there is an old pink-washed limestone house with the baking oven outside the wall, something he described in his journal when he visited the north of the island.

The forest is mixed here: large pine, birch and oak. In the fields maize is cultivated, but also wheat and barley. I pass Ajmund's bridge on the way towards Mästerby. It was here by the old waterway, the Suderting river, and the main road to Visby that the peasant army of Gotlanders had gathered in 1361 to try and stop the Danes and Valdemar Atterdag from marching to Visby. Legend has it that a witch

The apse, Mästerby church, with Byzantine paintings, partially painted over in 1633.

Shortly after our arrival here, thunder and lightning set in with rain, which wetted the soil which had now become parched, there having been no rain in all the time we had spent here in the land.

colluded with Valdemar under the bridge and spirited away the Gotlanders' strength. This place, this verdant quiet idyll, was the scene of one of the bloodiest battles in the Gotlanders' history. There is not much water in the river; I glimpse a trickle running amidst the yellow iris and mare's-tail.

Mästerby church is richly adorned with paintings from about the 13th to the 17th centuries. The most remarkable are the Byzantine murals in the Lady Chapel and in the apse. I fail to find the gravestone with the runic inscriptions. Outside the churchyard wall, modern agriculture greets us with a huge machine park of agricultural implements and bunting. In the well maintained meadow, enormous oaks form a clear boundary to the extensive fields where, so far at least, sugar beet continues to be grown. I notice that early purple orchid, military orchid and greater butterfly orchid flourish here, but most of them have finished flowering. By the bridge leading across a ditch which runs through the meadow there is a luxuriant dogwood bush.

The King's House at Roma is surrounded by yellow fields of wheat and sugar beet plantations. The sugar works have been discontinued and stand like a monument to one hundred years of agriculture and industry in Gotland. This is the fertile Roma plain at the edge of the drained Roma marsh. Straight avenues lead into the monastery precincts. The regional governor no longer occupies the King's House, and the magnificent byre which Linnæus noted has returned to being a monastery in ruins. But novel activities have entered the monastic precincts; Shakespearean plays are performed in the ruins every summer and have been so for more than 20 years, and in the main dwelling house and the wings there are galleries, a museum, arts and crafts, and Gotland crafts for sale. The monastic milieu is an attractive goal for tourists and draws large crowds.

Yet, the place is still redolent of the Middle Ages; relics from the excavated monastery ruin, lie behind the theatre stage, a monastery garden has been established behind the main building, and the abbot's house has been restored. The proud Romanesque architecture of the Cistercians is still there in portals and decorations in the residence. The former meadows of the monastery are now a large-scale farm, but remains of the monks' self-sufficient economy are evident in the surroundings, the two large carp ponds, for example, northwest of the monastery.

An avenue of trimmed trees once led to Sanda church. Today nobody manages the trees.

189

A Renaissance dinner laid out in the apse of Mästerby church

16 JULY (27 JULY) *In the morning we viewed the meadows and the fields. We found a plant which had not hitherto been observed in Sweden, growing plentifully on the roadside and was Cardus capitulo nutante (musk thistle) which grows plentifully near Paris (…)*

In the marsh meadow on the northern side of the marsh there was a plant which is annually consumed by the apothecaries in incredible quantities and had never before been found in Sweden. We have seen it a few times before both in Gotland and Öland, but quite tender so that one has not been able to touch it, but now it was obvious, for the flowers were beginning to open. It is called Scordium (water germander) by the apothecaries and grew in among the grass where the sedge began.

There was also Lycopus, Ultricularia, Ononis (gypsywort, greater bladderwort, restharrow) in plenty in the fields, vexatious to the ploughman as the plough is unable to pull up its hard roots, a reason why it is also called iron-root here (…) Here in the countryside lime trees are very rare, but rarer still is the alder, there is no beech at all.

In the afternoon we left here. We viewed the church, paid our respects to the dean, Martin Berg at Roma, travelled towards the town, having on either side beautiful meadows and delightful oak groves. The barley was now not wholly green, dried in patches. The farmer now hastened to bring in his hay which had already been cut in most of the meadows.

At ten o'clock in the evening we arrived in Wisby where we were given lodgings with the Head of the County Constabulary Mr Frigel and Inspector Lundmark.

Roma Abbey.

27 July

In 1164 when the Cistercian monks built their monastery Sancta Maria de Gutnalia at Roma, they did so on what was probably the most important site on the island. It was here at the Thing that all the free men had gathered in heathen times to pass judgement in disputes. This is where they held the sacred ring and swore their oaths to speak the truth. But new times were now drawing near with the church taking responsibility for what was right and wrong.

The Cistercians knew how to cultivate the soil, how to get crops to flourish. With its waterways across the marshes and its surrounding fertile soil, Roma was an ideal site.

The Roma plain still feels like one of the most fertile areas in the island. The marsh has been drained, the small fields and meadows have been combined into kilometre wide fields for large-scale farming. Walking in the direction of the old carp ponds, I see the flower which Linnæus had not previously come across in the country, and which the pharmacists used in large quantities, Scordium or water germander.

The Latin name is a distortion of the Greek word *skorodon*, garlic, and the plant has that smell when fresh. The pharmacies used the plant in their *teriak* [a mixture of medicaments used as an antidote to poison], the universal remedy of the time which, in addition to a series of Oriental spices such as cinnamon, myrrh, saffron, *nardus* [a drug made from roots of various plants], pepper and opium, also contained lizard and snake flesh. During the Renaissance *teriak* was principally imported from Venice and Nuremberg but, when Linnæus visited Gotland,

In summer evenings Shakespeare plays
are performed in the monastery; in the
daytime there are others who play.

the pharmacist in Visby had already the previous year produced his own very first *teriak* in the presence of the regional governor and the island's physician, who was also head of the secondary school.

There is nothing left of the marshlands around Roma where Linnæus wandered, but the rare water germander with its habitat in damp meadows and on lake shores has survived centuries of changes to the countryside.

The perfectly straight avenues lead up to the King's House from several directions. I imagine the avenue from the north to be of medieval origin and planned so as to make it possible to see the tower of the parish church from the monastery, something that was never achieved. Within, there is a chancel and a nave with two aisles from the 14th century and a closed up tower arch to the west. Maybe the plague intervened. The country road to Visby is lined with whitebeam. At Follingbo the fertile soil comes to an end; here limestone rock and gravel lie bare and only low pines scratch a bit of nourishment here and there from the limestone crevices.

The discontinued Roma sugar works.

Interior from the ruin of St Drotten, Visby.

28 July–5 August

Carl and his friends spent nine quiet days in Visby and its surroundings before they managed to get hold of a yacht that could carry them to Öland at a reasonable price. He was angry and frustrated at the poor communications via the mail boat, at the fact that the skipper was a drunkard, the boat was deficient, that it only operated very irregularly and that the "Authorities" did not care about the state of affairs. He had arrived in Gotland a week later than anticipated, the day tours on the island meant long working days and little sleep; it was hard to save up days. Now he was to be delayed even further. In Stockholm new times awaited him; just as he was about to embark on his journey to Öland and Gotland he had been informed of his appointment as Professor medecinae practicae at Uppsala University and had been granted leave of absence from the post until the autumn. A new life was soon awaiting him with the professorship he had so coveted.

Entries in his journal of the last nine days in the island are scantier than previously. He moves in the town's society circles and is invited out to dinner practically every night. The days are spent on the shores around the town where the party studied fossils and found the occasional plant which they had not discovered before. The descriptions of Visby are few: he notes that the old stone houses have a coal black crust and that is probably because they had been affected by lichen and not, as the party had thought at first, by soot from fires. The mulberry trees and walnut trees had succumbed during the harsh winter, but the lilacs had survived.

His notes mostly deal with such matters as he had not had the time to write down earlier, a seal hunt on Sandö island, for example, or the island export of raw materials, such as timber, lime and tar.

The departure takes a dramatic turn, and the description of the crossing to Öland in the printed travel account is a classic in its brevity and escalating drama. One sentence says it all:

"At half past five in the morning we embarked, at the risk of our lives we left the harbour in the breakers of a roaring sea, our friends and Wisby disappeared, the Carlsö islands came into sight, the north wind began howling, the waves raging, the ship was tossed between surging waves, Gotland disappeared, my companions were sea-sick, the tackle began to snap, despair entered our hearts and we committed ourselves into the hands of God (...)"

Today Visby in the last week of July and the first week of August is a town of tourists and for tourists. In the pleasant warm summer weather there are more outdoor restaurants than ever, night life is intensive, and most people do what Carl and his friends did on their last night in the island "graecando apud antipodes" that is, live like Greeks and turn night into day. I wonder how the working people of Visby cope with the high decibels in lanes and squares until the small hours. Do they all have triple glazing?

Visby which has been designated as a World Heritage Site by UNESCO and is one of the world's best preserved medieval towns shows a different aspect during these condensed summer weeks. Few people think of the fact that the streets are lined with ancient, closed 13th century storehouses and simple unspoilt wooden houses, that the cross alleys still have their old covering of flag stones and cobbles; most of them hidden by street cafés, souvenir shops and temporary stalls. Blinds, parasols, streamers and banderols conceal history. Anyone who wants to know and learn had better go to *Gotlands Fornsal* at the regional museum and the medieval oasis in the Chapter House garden where, according to his printed travel account, Linnæus found Bishop Wallin's beautiful library "which was charmingly arranged in the middle of his garden".

The genuine Visby is best experienced during other seasons. I visit some of the church ruins, but not even there do I find any sign of the authentic; preparations are going on for the annual medieval theatre

Ruin of St Karin, Visby.

and games. Instead I do as Carl and his friends did, turn my back on Visby this time and walk along the sea, enjoying the mild breeze and finding some trilobites and brachiopods along the shore towards the bathing place at Gustavsvik.

The boat traffic is more frequent than in the 18th century. Several large ferries lie waiting in the new harbour, south of the one Linnæus used. In the roads I see some cruise liners. This is where I bid Carl and his party farewell. I stay in Gotland to wait for autumn. Maybe then I will make another journey round of the island to see the migratory birds fly over the island and the vegetation take a rest? Or in the spring when hepatica and butterbur cover the slopes by the town wall and the goosander and long-tailed duck fill the air with expectant screams?

199

LIST OF BUILDINGS AND PLACES

TRANSLATOR'S NOTES

- The round brackets are as in the original version. Square brackets are the translator's addition for the sake of clarity or explanation.
- The word *fjärdingsväg* is an old Swedish measurement meaning a quarter of an old Swedish mil, equivalent to 2,762 metres.
- The translations from Latin are back translations of the Swedish texts.

GotlandsBoken AB
Vamlingbo Simunde,
623 31 Burgsvik
info@gotlandsboken.se

Copyright © Marita Jonsson 2007
Copyright © Photography Marita and Helga Jonsson 2007
Translation Eivor Cormack
Copyright © Photography p. 11 and 26 Ingalill Snitt
Map p. 4 Kungl. biblioteket/ photography Jessica Lund
Designer Elsa Wohlfahrt Larsson
Repro and print by Alfa Print AB, Sundbyberg 2007
ISBN 978-91-976508-2-3